Sum*thing*
of a mocktale

Sum*thing*
of a mocktale
at JNU where Kurta fell in Love with Jeans

SOMA DAS

Srishti
PUBLISHERS & DISTRIBUTORS

Srishti Publishers & Distributors
N-16 C. R. Park
New Delhi 110 019
srishtipublishers@yahoo.com

First published by Srishti Publishers & Distributors in 2007
Copyright © Soma Das, 2007

ISBN 81-88575-61-5

Typeset in AGaramond 11pt. by Suresh Kumar Sharma at Srishti

Cover design: Purba Rudra, Ajay Kumar, Ayusman Sarangi

Photographs: Purba Rudra, Amitabha Saxena

Printed and bound in India

Claims

Oath –

I swear by the JNU logo that I shall speak only lies, more lies and nothing except lies. I promise that I shall treat every rumour, every hearsay, Chinese whispers and oral folk tradition of JNU as the ultimate truth. I shall play down the virtues and highlight the vices. Over and above that I shall try my level best to spice up the lies to the fullest dramatic effect.

Declaration –

I declare I know no grammar. I shoot straight from the heart. At best this is my maiden step into the world of letters, a giant leap away from the literary world.

Letter to my reader –

Read the book if you have ever led a campus life, if you are living it now or will live one in future. If you are the *bindaas* type, you will relate; if you are the bookworm type, you will know what you are missing. Read it if you ever desired to know openly or secretly, the unofficial unedited account, if you believe in books that talk. Read this if you want to live life one degree fuller, if you want to have serious 'FUN'.

....and before you embark on this journey to Fun Island, you are requested to take off your thinking caps and reasoning hats.

....and please pray for the author's life after you finish reading. Personally I shall take all precautions to survive for my next book.

Acknowledgments

I must thank Rajasree, Latika and co. who laughed at the intended jokes in the book and not at the fact that *I* was penning it.

Not to forget people who took time out for me in spite of their tight schedules — Amitabha for lending his photography skills, Ayusman for his technical support even at 2 a.m., Kaushiki for her critical inputs.

My heartfelt gratitude to Purabi Panwar for editing, and Srishti team for their professional expertise and personal care.

I thank my darling super-busy brother Subrat for his enthusiasm and my entire family which is too big to be named here.

I also thank Butola Sir to have inculcated 'critical faculties' in us, to have taught us to look at things not the way they appear, but the way they do not. (Sorry Sir, to have misused the skill)

I am grateful to JNU which has imparted us the courage to laugh at our own-selves.

Finally, I thank my father for pushing me to the edge every-time I slackened and Mamuni for threatening to sleep off if I lengthened my narration.

…Thanking Ajay, Purba and Ma would be like distributing neighbourhood competition prizes to people who deserve a Nobel for their contribution in this project.

Contents

1

A Whole New World

People usually drink black coffee at nights in this corner of the world. Oh no no no......not that they are particularly fond of it, just that they are hardly left with a choice. They usually run out of milk powder pouches in their hostel rooms. When they don't, those pouches are emptied into containers of various shapes and sizes to innovate coffee concoction of kinds that can invite envy from coffee-houses, afterwards the pouches are used to polish the skill of an aiming game wherein you must master the art of flinging the trash directly into the dust-bin, no matter which spot of the cramped room you stand on.

Welcome to this crispy cottony handloomy world of JNU.

This is a place where it doesn't matter where you hail from, which fashion statements you made earlier......whether you wore chiffon salwar kameez, DKNY tank tops, nylon shirts with tiny mango motif prints over terycot trousers. This is the end of all diversities.

No one really knows what forces of standardization operate here, people consciously or subconsciously shed their individual tastes and preferences and submit to the great JNU tradition. Fab India in Vasant Kunj has strategically located its outlet.

Over and above the cotton unisex kurtas and ethnic chappals, the jhola is the final stamp of a JNUite.

Those who don't adhere to the above rule themselves feel alienated. So did I on my first day.

As I entered the campus through the cavernous North gate, I could already sense the distinct nature of this rocky Kingdom. This kind of lush continuum of greenery in Delhi, by itself could become tourist attraction. I had arrived on the scene.

Admin Block was my first destination where many comrades stood, moved about, waiting to help. Well, with an admission procedure lengthier and more cumbersome than a calculus sum we needed them.

"Hi! I am Sharmishtha. What about you?" a volunteer wearing her political affiliation in a badge greeted to offer her services.

"Kaya Pattnaik, CSODR."

"CSODR? Cool, do you know the full form?"

"Of course! Centre for Study of Obstacles in the Development of Regions."

"Well that is the superficial…I mean….. the official one. The de facto one is Centre for Suppression, Oppression, Depression and Repression."

I smiled back. "Really? Looks like I am in for some third degree torture." And thought to myself 'got to check the difference between suppression and repression in the dictionary'.

Sharmishtha was indeed helpful.

"First take a form, fill the entire 22 pages."

'22 pages? So, finally I get to author a book' my thought interrupted her admission speech that she blurted out like a waiter repeats his menu.

Sharmishtha went on "Stick a snap of yours on all the coloured folios. In all you would need 12 snaps, 8 for now, 4 for later. Go to the first room on left and submit your original certificate, and come back here, enter the hall, get an admin stamp on each page, go get it checked from the room where you submitted your originals. After checking, the man there gives you your folios. Fill all 8 folios, stick a snap on each. Submit the red one in School of Social Sciences-II building, green one in hostel, blue in DSW (Department of Student Welfare) building, yellow one here in admin, pink one in stadium, orange one with the finance department, violet with the centre and white one is for you."

"Thanks" I said, exhausted already.

Murmuring to myself where to submit which colour folio, I spent my entire day with pan chewing JNU staff, many of them pretending to be more important than the Vice Chancellor. By the time I went back home I knew I must have cleared some great exam or why else would the procedure be so long?

That night I dreamt of myself running in slow motion.....amidst lush green grass, looking nothing less than a Yash Chopra heroine......with folios of all colours raining from the sky.

Next day I didn't have the luxury of my dad's car. I had to board 615, I mean the bus, which was to become my fate for the next two years that I was to spend in JNU.

I wore a pastel shade salwaar kameez for the first day. On the bus my anxiety made me scream to the conductor "Bhaiya please let me know when we reach JNU."

He shouted back fighting the roaring ignition of the DTC bus "Don't worry." After what must have been 45 minutes he frantically waved at me "The next stop, *medam* the next one is JNU stop." I hurriedly stomped past the standing crowd stamping on a few unknown feet to the gate and stumbled on the metal steps.

I began my journey on the only road that could take me inside JNU. I stopped to ask a guy through his thick specs under umbrella. "How far is CSODR?"

"That is at the fifth bus stop; you got down on the first stop only. Doesn't matter, you walk down, just a 20-25 minutes walk from here" he said.

I thought 'It is already time for the first class. If I walk for 25 minutes; I will miss approx three fourth of class.'

Realising I had no choice, I made a note in my mind - first lesson of the day: my official address would be fifth bus stop from now on.

As I trudged on, with beads of perspiration forming a necklace on my forehead on that sunny July morning, a loud Bhojpuri song burst out in the backdrop. It turned many heads. One of the heads was mine.

By the time I figured out that the noise shot out of an auto-rickshaw with plastic multi-coloured flower bouquets near its headlight, the auto simply zoomed past me, splattering yesterday's rain water on my new pastel salwar suit.... painting modern art on a canvas.......which could just fetch abuses had I not been decent.

Meanwhile a glimpse of the giggling duo, inside the auto, settled in my mind.

With sweat on my body and mud on my suit, I feared nothing. It took me three wrong turns, many interruptions to reconfirm the route and 35 minutes to find my way to the Centre and I wondered whether it was worthwhile to attend whatever little of the class that was left. From outside the lecture hall I could hear noises, the types that students make when teacher is not there. I peeped in and found my hunch was right.

There were a few girls in flowery kurtas with jute bags by their side which had an image of Goddess Durga on them with a message in Bengali:

Mazumdar Saree Bhandar, Gariyahat, Kolkata.

I introduced myself, "Kaya, DU."

Two of the girls gingerly let out their names in disinterested voices, more as a favour, ignored me and resumed their chatting. The one with blue flowers seemed interested.

"Urboshee. See *toh*, Sir did not come. With such difficulties I managed to come this early..." and she appointed me her agony aunt. I don't want to bore you with her troubles, my eyes wandered ahead.

After four flowery kurtas, there was a flowery shirt, his flowers smaller. His nose screwed up for some weird reason. I moved to him "What about you?"

Urboshee answered for him "*Pinaki Shannal*, he was the only guy in Presi (Presidency college) among 20 of us," she winked at me.

"*Aieee*, why are you replying on my behalf?" Pinaki retorted back then went on *gad gad* in Bengali. I moved on.

There was only one handsome hunk but he was whiter than talcum and had an expressionless deadpan for a face. He kept fanning himself with the lean pad that he had brought to take notes.

For once, a smiley face popped up from behind introducing himself. "Sukamal Baruah, Cotton College, Assam. And you?"

I introduced myself and returned to white face. White face shifted his fan from right to left hand and managed "Taran *yaar*, from Kullu Govt. College. I am living here with Toramal Thakur Sir *yaar*. He is from Laddakh, my uncle's friend's own brother. This class is his *yaar*, he told me he will come I don't know what happened *yaar*."

My mind wavered to imagine Toramal Sir. *Potbellied, bald headed, nearing 60.* My concentration was broken by giggles and I turned back to find the giggling duo from the auto.

They were in my class!

The giggling duo included a guy who had a voice like Amrish Puri but a walk like Bipasha Basu. He seemed a perfect case of "wanna be hip" with his yellow floater, hanging jeans, T-Shirt with *Ram-Ram* written all over, tulsi bead around his neck, goatee and a dumbo-bumpkin face.

The girl looked cute in her small flouncy pony and bell bottoms. She said "Oh so sorry! You were the girl on the road!"

Both of them were from Hansraj College, DU. Ragini probed everybody present about their percentage in Graduation and made known that she was the University topper without being asked.

Our second class had commenced. Prof. Naqvi looked like sweet grandpa. We all started listening intently, the Bengali girls with pen and notebooks taking notes of God-knows-what. He was just introducing us to the geography of JNU which was obviously not in the course. But his lecture did seem interesting.

"The map of JNU has been constructed keeping in mind the map of India, you know that. The north of JNU is called Uttarakhand, the suffix *khand* because in north India that is the local word for region, where the hostels of Ganga, Satluj, etc. are located. Similarly, Dakshinapuram is the southern region, *puram* as you hear in Mahabalipuram etc where you have Godavari, Periyar and Kaveri. The western part of JNU is known as

Paschimabad, *bad* as in Ahmedabad, where Naramada, Tapti, Mahi, Sabarmati hostels are located signifying the rivers flowing in Western India. On the same lines, we have Purvanchal, which has Mahanadi, Brahmaputra hostels."

The class was amazed, Pinaki's hand went up. Pinaki's index finger rose over other fingers which were closed in a fist. "But *Saar, whyee* there is no Madhya Pradesh?" This finger, a nuisance we were to witness thereafter in every class, several times.

Naqvi had to take up the challenge, so his grin became wider, a half moon turning into a new moon. "Son here we are talking about directions like North, South, East, West and Centre is not a direction, OK!"

Pinaki did not look satisfied.

Naqvi continued "How the buildings in JNU are narrow at the bottom and grow wider towards the top floors signify the process of growth as seen in a tree."

Pinaki whispered from behind "But that is an incorrect way of construction. The base of the building should be wider and stronger than the rest." Naqvi went on and on about JNU's history, geography, sociology, psychology, ideology and more.

The flowery girls must have noted everything in their notebook. The class was finally over and we all were hypnotized to believe that we were the blessed ones to have cleared a national exam and enter an institution which will change our lives with the magic wand of knowledge.

No other class was to be taken on the first day. So, along with Ragini and Adhbhut, I set off to explore the campus. I couldn't explain how but there was an instant bonding.

For today, we chose the food joint *Teflas*. Adhbhut took out his bright yellow walkman and orange earphones coordinated with his floaters. Ragini asked me a few questions from here and there "Do you have a pet? I had one, a fish, her name was Champa Bai but we called her CB at home." A fish.... petname....at home...goodname...at office!

We strolled to the food joint '*Teflas*' where Adhbhut met one of his old Bihari friends and joined him at his table. Ragini said she wasn't really hungry to which I thought 'it doesn't look good if we sit with an empty table in a food joint' so I checked out the right side of the menu. Veg chowmein was the cheapest – Rs. 11.50. I ordered one. Ragini confined in me on how she had never spoken to this Bihari guy, Adhbhut, even once during the three years in college but now it was different. Since they were the only ones to be commuting from the far off North Campus of Delhi University, she had to be friendly with him.

Our chowmein arrived steaming hot. Since Ragini had already declared that she was full, it was out of sheer formality that I fetched two forks and offered her one. She rolled some noodles around her fork and took a bite. After that bite I did not have to offer her next time because she didn't stop eating till the plate looked as if it had been washed with detergent. Finally pushing the plate aside she took a deep breath and asked "How many bro-and-sis?"

I replied "Two sisters, including me."

"We are three. Rimjhim, Ragini and Roshmita, my parents' last attempt to have a son." The water choked in my throat, I had never heard something like this before. Ragini spoke her mind, most of the time.

After that she excused herself to meet some of her friends Zuri, Shabari, Tribeni in Godavari hostel to fix up a place to shift in illegally till a hostel room was allotted to her.

8

I asked Adhbhut if he wanted to take a 615 with me. He nodded and we walked back to the bus stop expressing our views on some national issue of substance, mainly pretending intellect, not so much out of real concern. As we were deeply engrossed in debating on national security issues on the stop, a stray dog walked straight to us as if we shared some special relationship. I suffer from serious **dog phobia**. I tried to hide behind Adhbhut just when I realized that he too was trying to use me as a shield against the dog. Security issues of the nation… two experts..sure.

Much to our relief, an approaching 615 saved us further embarrassment and we hurriedly got into the bus. A two seater was empty on the ladies' side. While I was still wondering whether it would be appropriate to leave Adhbhut standing and sit on the seat, he made the move.

He confidently walked past me to grab the window side of the ladies seat and gave me a sardonic look "You first talk of equal gender rights and then ask for extra rights at every step." I settled on the seat besides him.

His bright earphones now adorned around his ears looking kind of weird on his round bumpkin face. He tapped his feet and hands with the music. A real connosieur who could enjoy music even amidst sweat, heat and crowd.

Half way through, I could feel his head on my shoulders. Shocked I stretched my neck to look his side; he was fast asleep with his mouth wide open. Then I thought it was quite undignified to sleep like that in a public bus.

But then I also saw an opportunity – till he slept I could listen to some music. I slowly pulled out the earphones leaving the walkman in his hands so as not to disturb him out of his slumber. I placed it on my ear and my expression changed. The earphone spoke into my ears "*Our constitution, Subhash Kashyap Part III Fundamental Rights, Fundamental Right Article 14 states that.......*"

I froze "Oh God! This guy is here for Civil Services and he is already preparing polity for the General Studies paper even in the bus."

It sent a shudder down my spine suddenly having realized the level of commitment people of my age could have while I roamed around clueless.

I placed his earphones back. A stop before mine, I woke him up and bid goodbye. "By the way what music are you listening to?" I asked.

He replied "Eminem. Do you want it? You can borrow the cassette from me next week."

I smiled back "No thanks, I am more the Hindi songs type" and waved him good bye.

✦

2

HIV Seeds to Epistemological Violence

The diversity that is missing in the dressing sense of JNU is compensated by the faculty. Even if I miss one of them, the narration would remain incomplete but due to space and time constraints I have resorted to random sampling.

All of us have mastered the chapter of sampling, thanks to Dubey Sir, who taught us sampling in the first four months of our first semester. The rest of the course which included mean, median, mode, quartile, standard deviation, variance, correlation, regression....... he managed in the last one and a half months. So by random sampling I choose a few of my faculties who I decide to dissect here.

- Objective of the study: To display the range of faculty that JNU offers
- Database: CSODR teaching staff
- Methodology: Observation and exaggeration
- Interpretation

Overenthusiastic Bichitra Roy: Flowers in Pinaki's shirt were in full bloom. He had made a mark i.e. he had been noticed by most of the teachers mainly for the following reasons –

(a) He asked questions in every class so Profs did not want to irk him for the fear that his questions might grow more complicated.

(b) He had not changed his flowery shirt for 16 days in a row so Profs did not have problems recognizing him.

Back to Bichi Roy: She looked younger than her age, this we guessed from her daughter's age. She was dedicated, enthusiastic and unorganized. She came to class with her mesh of thoughts and presented them in even messier manner.

Bong girls showered Bichi Roy with abundant head nods in the class which boosted Roy's confidence but the moment the class got over, the same lot would surround her outside the lecture hall to probably redo a short Bengali version of what exactly transpired in the class.

Once when Bichi Roy was explaining "You know......hmm....what happens is that....hmm....when people are not exactly employed but....hmm still are employable... hmm..*maane* do you understand...ok leave it." Her fingers conveyed more than her speech "Assume an eligible person is studying...hmm then he is paying some fees...hmm....but the same economic person is also forgoing the salaries....hmm....that he would have earned had he been not studying."

Pat popped a voice from amongst us "Opportunity cost." We hardly had to look back. It had to be Pinaki. He had hit bull's eye. Bichi's expression said it all. Opportunity cost had formed a bond between Bichi and Pinaki which was to remain solid as rock for all semesters to come. That day of "Opportunity cost" and all the days after that, in Bichi Roy's class we knew who the second in command was.

The next one on dissection table is **Prof. Bhanumati Sahu.**

Well what about her. I think her first class would suffice. She started every second sentence of hers with "I don't know but…" On that, students used to fill in the blank before she could "If you don't know then why talk about it."

In her first class she embarked on a green journey "I don't know but I think all of you should have heard about Green Revolution. Well the basic contributor to this revolution was HIV seeds." We didn't know whether we heard it right but she continued unperturbed, unfettered "HIV seeds once sown on fertile land can do wonders. HIV seeds can multiply the product many times as has happened in India during 1960s….so do you all agree about the beneficial effect of HIV seeds?"

An insignificant voice blurted "No Ma'am." And Ragini murmured next to me "Oh God! Is she actually talking about HYV, High Yielding Variety seeds!"

"Very good, HIV seeds are not all that beneficial. Apart from imbalance regarding development and the cost factor, can you point out another demerit?"

"Yes Ma'am, it can cause AIDS" I don't think the insignificant voice listened to the lecture at all. Quite early in the semester, we had given up on Bhanu and Bhanu had given up on us.

Remember **Toramal Thakur**? The one who had played host to the white faced Taran Sharma. He didn't emerge remotely close to my imagination. He was anything but baldheaded, potbellied and old. But with a name like Toramal (which sounds more like a seth-jewelers name), what did you think I would expect?

To cut short, he was a good looking import from the US who drew a few "oohs" "aahs" and "oh maas" in my class. He had looks and importantly, an accent. I wonder how people who spend 30 years of their lives in remote Laddakh and 3 years abroad put on such accents. Well that was all he had, looks and accent.

Neither his knowledge permitted him to teach us, nor did he ever bother to prepare for the classes. Like lovers, we quietly, without words, reached an agreement. An unspoken *MoU* was signed. He gave good grades to everyone and we were not to open our mouth on our misgivings about him.

But the icing on cake is yet to be taken up-**Birendra Bahuguna**.

If it were in my capacities I would paste a snap of his rather than describe him. This lean, sporty, hyperactive Prof. with hyper reflex action was overstuffed with knowledge. Again if I had played a part in his naming ceremony I would have christened him with a more radical name like "Henry Vivian Derozio" or something more bombastic.

He was an out and out radical communist. Students who visited his home swore that his living room exhibited portraits of Marx, Lenin and SFI (Students Federation of India, the student wing of communist parties) posters.

Two things need special mention. His hair stood upright on his head, toothbrush bristle, defying gravity like a bed of thorns and he himself looked like a leaner replica of Marco Polo, Einstein or somebody great.

The first day while he lectured us on ontological and epistemological violence, Ragini and I were busy exchanging notes.

Ragini passed on her note "I can't picture him on anything other than a bicycle."

"Don't be mean, that is such a classist comment. Anyway he owns a red Maruti 800."

"Gosh I knew he has communist leanings. But even his car is red. Wonder what colour his soul is?"

"What all is he talking about? Too hi-fi. Go sit on his head so that he shuts up"

She answered "Those thorns will hurt *Yaar*"

But to be honest, I eventually started liking his class as his was the only class that offered us novelty and amusement and "critical faculty" as he himself put it.

He questioned everything, put a conspiracy angle to the most innocent of social norms and explored the unapparent processes resulting in the phenomena that we all accepted unquestioningly.

Once he lectured us on body politics-a limited body space which is bombarded by information from all directions. In the same class he told us how in today's world, information reigns supreme, how wisdom is lost in knowledge and knowledge is lost in information.

While half the class laughed and the other half dozed off in a siesta, I seemed to find it interesting. Another day he pointed out how the mall-culture sharpens the divide between rich and poor. As he rightly remarked that although for the heck of it The Ansal Plaza is open to all ...

"How many lower middle class and lower class people do you spot there? How many slum dwellers would dare to enter the glass building that screams 'only for those who can afford'. The construction of the building itself is so intimidating that it perpetuates class distinction by making a poor man feel nauseated and left out if he chose to visit it. With the invasion of malls , what would become of the good old bazaar, a space where class distinctions melted away, where millionaires jostled among the rest of the crowd, where the prosperous rubbed shoulders with poor to pop in street food. Now the kids of those millionaires wouldnot even know that their counterpart Chhotu is serving tea at a *chchee-chchee* unhygienic place where

Chhote sahib can't stand to eat."

The class connotation of malls had appealed to me. I couldn't stop thinking of Chhotu next time I visited a mall.

He had an intellectual insight on the weirdest of things. For example, how gender is objectified by manufacturing a Coke bottle whose shape conforms to a female figure. Whenever a man holds a Coke bottle he feels he possesses woman and this entire process consolidates the already entrenched patriarchy.

Till date, he appears to be the most underrated, joked about Prof. both by students and faculty. But if I found anybody promising in the first semester, it was him. Either we had the same wavelength of madness, or he remained grossly misunderstood like most geniuses because they were much ahead of their times.

Before we move ahead, I will introduce a person who was with me and Ragini all this while. Ragini and I were not the dynamic duo. Shubhra, Ragini and I were the tempestuous trio of which Ragini and I were the tempest and Shubhra, the rehabilitation centre. She was an exotic combination of divinity and laziness. She was goodness personified and we respected her immensely in our hearts but were too embarrassed to admit it as it did not seem cool. As for her laziness it was a selective attribute, it appeared only at sight of textbooks.

Assume her presence all through the book with me and Ragini even if her name does not figure frequently. Actually she was too good, and this narration too nasty for her.

3

"Maa Go" – The Bold and Beautiful

Back to business after all that goodness. Well there is something about Bongs of CSODR. I chose to call the club "Maa Go". You could have had your pick "*Oh Maa*", "*Baari Jaabo*" or "*Naaa Re*" or whatever. They give you ample catchy punch lines and rewind and replay it hundred times a day till it deeply registers in some corner of your mind unnoticed. And in some tense crisis ridden moment you might let go of a … "Maa Go", then bite your tongue between your teeth, look around to check whether you were caught.

CSODR Bongs are hundred percent Homosapiens but a different sub species within it. Of the total 16 girls, 9 were Maa Go club members, so you can well imagine the plight of the rest. The mini-Bengal dominated mini-India by virtue of numerical majority but I suspect they would reign over even if they hadn't had numbers on their side. Rumpa, Jhumpa, Tumpa, Shampa …the Pa dynasty we hear had invaded CSODR shortly after its inception and had been ruling supreme since generations.

Ragini and I felt what *doi-machh* must feel lying infront of *Bengali bhadralok*, what *butter-chicken* must feel after being served to a Punjabi family with serious appetite, what the black dogs must feel in vicinity of Naga tribes, in short, ready to be gobbled down, only to resurface in form of a belch. Although Shubhra was a Bong too she didn't fit into the Maa Go club as she lacked the defining traits.

The remainder Maa Go club narrowed towards its tail, with a sole representative from the other half of the society, Pinaki Sanyal keeping the *bhadralok* torch alight, fiercely protected by his female counterparts.

Well, classes had begun in full swing. While I spent most of my time snoring in bus no. 615, occasionally my head tumbling down on unknown shoulders (where I once found Adhbhut's sleeping undignified), Shubhra used her precious hours to solve crossword puzzle with the seriousness of scientists on the verge of invention, Ragini indulged most of her time trying new dresses and measuring the millimeters of fat that she had put on various parts. The days she felt her arms had finally lost those meaningful millimeters of fat, she decided those were the days the world should see her arms and she wore sleeveless.

She should have taken some lessons from the Maa Go club. Instead Maa Go club was inspired by Ragini. One by one all members shed their sleeves to display their bounty arms. Their rising confidence meter those days was a controversial topic to comment on. Their make over was treat to some, torture to others, comic to some, tragic to most.

It is a little too mean on my part to comment on their dressing sense. I myself am not sounding anything less than the fanatics who commented on Sania Mirza's short skirts. But believe me the transition in the girls is too important for my nasty narration, can't give it a miss.

Most of them did come with a wardrobe of flowery salwar-kurtas and tapering stretchable jeans from Cal (when bootcuts were in fashion). But they smoothly made the transition to the JNU tradition. The flowers in their kurtas wilted and were replaced by mirrors and vegetable dyes but what stayed on as a touch of originality was, body hugging fit of kurtas. And of course the self designed elaborate intricate necklines. But the club also trained themselves and fine tuned their academic skills during the time I snored, Ragini changed clothes and Shubhra solved crosswords.

Their senior Maa Go club had passed on cogent *guru mantras* and they fiercely guarded the prized possessions of notes inherited from seniors. They were more secretive about those notes than Ragini and I were about our love letters. But notes were not the whole of their assets. The mantras included a holistic approach for an all round personality development. Strategies to hit the bird in the eye.

Pinaki inaugurated the implementation of the strategy when he fell in love with Janvi and they were often caught coochie-cooing under public gaze, in Kamal Shopping Complex, near Administrative Block, at Nilgiri Dhaba. Janvi was arguably prettier than Pinaki but their love did not hold any future mainly for the following reasons:

1) Janvi was a respected member of a distinguished Prof's family.

2) Janvi could never ever carry forward Pinaki's family line. No no ... don't misunderstand, I'm not revealing any flaw in her reproductive system, how am I to know such private things. It is just that nature had been cruel enough to make her a canine.

I had already heard hush-hush gossips about Pinaki and Janvi, but that fateful evening I bumped into them. They were out on an evening stroll oblivious of the piercing gaze of passersby. I asked "Hey Pinaki, won't you introduce me to her?" He replied with a heartfelt smile that seemed genuine "She is *Beechi* Madam's baby *doggess*. Isn't she cute?"

"Yeah very cute," I the dog-phobic made up.

I think in more than one way the Maa Go club had learnt, adapted and evolved more than the rest of us and ought to be congratulated.

For their academic accomplishment they had a readymade recipe from Senior Maa Gos for which essential ingredients included -2 tablespoon of praise for Prof., 3 tablespoon of laughing at the PJs that Profs crack, 3 tablespoon of letting the Prof. know about your parent's dream about you doing well in JNU, 2 tsp of tears (strictly two tsp as an overdose can spoil the taste) and 2 tablespoon of charity at Prof's home, garnished by a selfless smile. All this and notes according to your taste will definitely work.

Well it did work for most of them but you must understand that all this calls for a lot of hard work and it called for a holistic personality to perform this herculean exercise. All credit to the Maa Go club. Together, they could do it. And together they did it. They kept the torch of tradition burning and I am sure their achievements would inspire our future Maa Go members to outperform the present generation.

Note: Here I must confess that I was nowhere remotely close in the running for any academic brownies which were distributed and redistributed among Maa Gos. So, all this cynicism could be the result of a frustrated and bitter subconcious.

While the Maa Gos burnt their midnight oil, I was still busy snoring in 615. Ragini was still super busy in trying out different dresses of the same kind and Shubhra besides solving crossword had acquired a skill of sorting and collecting caps of Colgate paste and Garnier lotions from roadside to replace the caps that Ragini had a habit of losing because by now Shubhra and Ragini had moved into the same hostel room in Tapti.

It was a pain to go shopping with the Maa Go club members. A shopping trip with them could end up with myriad experiences and a sense of definite deprivation. Once an avid member of the club, Rumpa, had fallen out with other members due to some intra club politics, in most likelihood over not sharing some exclusive ground-breaking notes, and cajoled me into the trap by shedding a few tears and scaling up the urgency of her need to shop for *Pujo*. I in turn pulled along Ragini and Shubhra by blackmailing them emotionally.

As we clambered into a crowded 615 bus, Rumpa embarked on the whimpering spree "In Calcutta, the metro takes care of you completely. Calcutta is bustling with people but the way Metro handles it there, Delhi can only dream of. No eve-teasing or adam teasing there *baba*."

Our first stop was a shoe store, a reputed one. The four of us walked to a smiling attendant "Yes *medam*"

Rumpa plunged herself on the settee and lifted both her feet towards the attendant. Pointing towards them, she asked "Can you show something for them" as if they were her kids.

After trying out what must be fifteen pair of shoes, she seemed to compromise on one pair. But on price enquiry, she fumed "What? *Seexhundredfifty* rupees and no discount, what are your shoes made up of, gold? Sometime you must visit Calcutta Khadims and Sree Leathers where better quality durable stuff is available for half the price." She resolved against buying shoes in Delhi ever after and lectured the attendant on how the shop was looting helpless, innocent customers.

When Maa Go members get really angry, they don't realize but they lose control over that weapon called tongue. Unaware they ooze out *matrubhasha* Bengali, peppered with a Hindi word here and there. And thankfully so. This way the other party doesn't understand most of the things and sometimes smiles back in innocence and ignorance.

That day Rumpa made us visit scores of shoe stores, undergarment shops, utensils shops and nightie shops. In all, time we spent in the scorching sun was some 4-5 hours. The output was a pink plastic mug and a red bucket, everything else could wait, after all Durga Puja was just a month and half away. When she visits Cal, she could do the rest of the shopping.

But during the shopping expedition, Ragini had bought three kurtas with borrowed money from the other three, each paying for one. (Beware Ragini has Obsessive Compulsive Disorder or OCD). She is a *pucca shopaholic* and if she has been behaving extra goody-goody with you since last 3-4 days, these are clear symptoms of the impending threat. In most probabilities she is going to demand money. The above model has a very high predictive value.

A shopping expedition or an outing with Rumpa could leave you an informed consumer

- At Shakuntalam theatre, she remembered "Nothing can beat *Nandan* at Cal, the seats, the rates, even the choice of movies there is better."

- Stuffing *golgappas* at *Khatta Meetha*, Sarojini Nagar "*Puchkas* at Victoria Memorial any day better, oh maa *Baari jaabo.*"

- A *kulfi faluda* at Aggrawal Sweets reminded her of "Putiram's *Radhaballabhi bheeshan* miss *karchhee*.I understand the importance of K.C. Das and Bhim Chandra Nag today.Have to head home, *Baari jaabo.* "

- Watching a movie at Priya complex, she grew nostalgic of Globe and New Empire theatre at Cal.

- Walking the streets of Sarojini Nagar, she whined " It is an all right market but the choice is limited, not like the New Market of Cal, it is a very old market, probably of British era."

- Sometimes the complains grew downright outrageous "You know when it rains in Cal, the earth there smells more humane than Delhi" (eyes filled with nostalgia)

When this unquenched thirst grew unbearable, the Maa Gos headed for *Chittaranjan Park* to have a meal at *Babu Moshai* only to come back and sigh "This is nothing like the real thing, it is more of a *pseudo-Bangla* culture adulterated heavily with Delhi culture" hastily adding "not that Delhi really has a culture to call its own. Want to go home, counting days, *Baari jabo.*"

Every time the group entered the class they burst out into a chorus-anthem "*Baari Jaabo*" in prolonged shrill tone as if they are performing for a Rabindra Sangeet Concert. What I always failed to understand was why couldn't they remember their homes in solitude, back in their hostel room? Or may be they did that too.

What you couldn't take away from Maa Gos was their inherent rich sense of culture. Each one of them was talented and apart from their academics, fashion, extra curricular activities (to be discussed in detail later) they still managed to impress us with their cultural traits. All of them could sing, dance and paint beautifully and often gave us an inferiority complex. How could everyone do everything?

The extra curricular that I promised I would discuss in detail was about sensuousness of the spicy Bong babes in my class. Barring two or three, who remained stranded on the other pole, refusing to change, rest of Maa Gos were overstuffed with sensuality so much so that even when they prayed, they crooned with more oomph than devotion. On the oomphometer scale, while 2 Maa Gos scored .02 and 1 respectively, rest ranged from a bright 8 to 10 and one particular lass crossed all boundaries.

Kakoli often punctuated her mundane talks with unnecessary oohs, aahs on which a guy commented innocently in the class "I think Kakoli is keeping unwell most of these days. Lately I have noticed she puffs and pants. Does she suffer from asthma?" I chose to reserve my comments on that while the one who scored .02 generally squeezed her nose up, whenever a guy came close to her.

The one who scored low in the oomphometer maintained a stern-stiff expression if a guy was seen within a one meter radius. If he tried inching closer, she mostly used her Cambridge accent as a weapon to ward him off and hence was christened "Engli".

Once she confided in me over coffee "Not that I haven't had a boyfriend in my life. I have been there, seen it all, done it all."

I replied in shock and disbelief, knowing her well enough "What is that supposed to mean?"

"Meaning, I had a boyfriend, with whom I had also gone out for a movie where he tried to hold my hand. Just look at his guts."

I got mean and inquisitive, gulped down the hot coffee in one go "And what happened then?"

"Then I didn't want to create a scene in the movie hall. So I excused myself to go to the loo. I got up, came out, took the next bus to home and never ever spoke to him again."

That day her rating on the oomphometer crashed to an all time low.

There were a few Maa Gos who sustained their high scores on oomphometer by developing unique-original traits. Tumpa often played a particular game with guys around. She scribbled with her finger tips vague things on their back, that they were supposed to guess.

Jhumpa was secretively named *Dhuk Dhuk*. Whenever she entered a jam session, the audience was thrilled, specially the guys and she didn't disappoint them, a hot item number ensued. Dozens of girlfriends had numerous complaints against her after those sessions.

Shampa who blasted the oomphometer, swore a dozen times by her boyfriend back home in Calcutta and his loyalty (but who the hell doubted her boyfriend's loyalty, we are talking about somebody else's loyalty here). She used her love back home as a license to free existence, and on any accusation from any quarter got furious "Don't forget I am committed to my beau, I badly miss him and we shall positively marry by next October. So don't even discuss these rumours with anyone. It can create misunderstandings between us. Just because I had a little fun doesn't mean that I am hooked with someone." Those days I wondered whether she was trying to remind us or her own self about her beau waiting at home. But oh dear, none of us were blind, though we did pretend that we were. For further details of her deeds please consult Jackie Collins and Nancy Friday.

The cutest part of Maa Gos were their earnest efforts to learn Hindi. More often than not these efforts fell flat for their love for

Bengali was too overwhelming to make space for another language. A few philanthropic guys who extended help in teaching Hindi to our Maa Gos, predictably, ended up enriching their own vocabulary of Bengali. Much after the failed efforts you spotted them forming an "O"with mouth and keeping it intact for as long as they tried their hand at freshly learnt Bengali.

Jokes aside, I must confess that however much I gossip about the Maa Go group, I loved them dearly for they were the colour in our dull and boring lives. Without them life in JNU would be a mango out of which juice has been sucked out. I loved the way they did the weirdest of things with great conviction and élan while we became conscious and lost out on real fun in life. If by any parameter the Western Society (read the US) sets standard of liberty, then the Maa Go group is closer to them than the rest of us. I could take such liberties with them only because of their wide latitude of acceptance.

"Way to go Maa Go club." I love you and miss you.

They have scattered and sobered down.

4

Bargaining Grades

In our first lecture, we were informed that JNU doesn't believe in the concept of toppers and therefore it follows a credit based grading system. Bahugna Sir warned us with a tight face "Here you have to EARN your grades" stressing on the earn making it sound as if grades were wage or salary, only you couldn't buy anything with that currency.

After the class, I climbed down the stairs to bump into a smily senior, Deboshree who was coming up. Deboshree seemed the right choice to clarify doubts. I apprehensively queried "How exactly does the grading system work here?"

She invited me for a cup of coffee in the canteen "If you are free, you might as well come with me. The grading system is a concept that I can explain to you in 5-10 minutes." I tagged along. That day she gave me the finite *gyan* of grades. "OK now listen to me carefully… Shambhuji, send me two cups of coffee and a *Vada Sambar*. What will you have?"

"Nothing, thanks."

"No you must."

"No thanks."

"That's the rule, you have to. OK have one *samosa* at least. After all you have come to the canteen for the first time with me. Seniors in CSODR are known for their generosity in the whole of JNU."

Without waiting for a reply, she shouted "Shambhuji send one *samosa* also."

Deboshree then reclined on the plastic chair to commence with her lecture "OK where were we? The grades. See there are slots and you yourself are the enlightened one to decide what you want. If you spend months of sleepless nights, cram all the notes, stop combing, stop taking bath and study, you will get A-only. If you just submit your assignment on time, read the questions, go write coolly, you will manage an A-minus which is still considered decent. If you miss a few assignments, just mug up the answers, vomit them out in end-semester exams, you will still manage a B-plus."

Dunking the oil dripping vada into sambar she continued "But, if you are here to do something else, like IAS-YAS, no …no I am not asking you that question. It is a highly personal question…I have better manners than that… so if you miss a few more assignments and just scribble anything in the exams, you will get B only. If you don't do most of the assignments, miss a paper or two in the end sems, you will be the benchmark….from below that is… with a B minus. Believe me if you cross that and manage a C, you will create a record in the history of CSODR. Your name will not be forgotten in years to come."

After her exhaustive speech I posed the million dollar question "And what about A plus?"

She put the last bite of vada in her mouth and smiled "Well say it is something like the moon and the stars, only decorative pieces" and then lowered her pitch to whispers "take my word for it, it is not even worth it. For example, even if you fetch moon and star from the sky, of what use are they here? Anyway, you have to make an important decision now. Once bracketed into a particular slot it is almost impossible to break the mould and move into another." Suddenly she looked at her watch and bit her tongue. "Oh my God, it's time for the class". She picked up her jhola, hurriedly got up and waved me goodbye.

When I got up, still pondering over my slot, lost in my maze of thoughts, Shambhuji stood on my head. "Madam Rs. 18 please."

I felt stupid "Oh sorry, *Bhaiya*" and paid him his bill.

By a day or two, I had zeroed down upon my slot "A-minus would do. Fair enough, what say?"

Ragini replied "Will do. *Arre karna kya hai?* As it is they don't believe in toppers."

Shubhra added "For me, even B plus would do." So the decision was arrived at.

On top of this, once Prof Bichi informed us "JNU believes in continuous internal assessment. Therefore, your end sems are just another exam. Anyway we have an open exam system where question papers are handed over to you much before you take the exam."

I exclaimed "How progressive? Wow! Not for nothing that JNU is called the Harvard of Third World."

The assignments were a different ballgame. Once they were graded, you still had the field open for negotiation. Once when I went to pick up a certain assignment to a certain Prof's cabin, I was stunned by the conversation brewing inside. I could hear a classmate's shaken voice.

"Sir, whenever I pick up this Rotoring pen, my hand shakes. It starts shivering, Sir. May be because I don't have a geography background. Haven't learnt all this ever, I must have torn four assignments before I submitted you this one Sir—the fifth one. Sir don't you think I deserve an A-minus on humanitarian grounds?......Thank you, Sir, thanks a lot."

Another time I overheard a girl's voice "Sir how fair do you think it is to compare me, hailing from a remote Gorakhpur University, with somebody who has been trained in Delhi University or Calcutta University? I do my best and you still do not consider....." As I heard sobs, I tip-toed away for the fear of being caught eavesdropping. Seconds after that, as I stood at a safe distance in the other end of the corridor, I spotted the girl emerging out of the room all smiles.

Whoops! I thought, how I wish bargaining grades was my cup of tea. Not that I never tried. I went to the same Prof. and like a fool demanded "Don't you think I deserved an A-minus?"

"And why do you think so?" the Prof gave a cold stare.

Startled by his retort, I managed meekly "Well...I ...kind of...have shown tremendous improvement."

"Over whom?" He didn't give up.

But in a way, I did "Over....over myself. I mean, if you don't reward me today, why would I feel like improving tomorrow?"

"Come next time *beta*." He politely shooed me away.

"No more bargaining grades for me. I shall EARN it for myself." I vowed and promised to myself.

But promises are made to be broken. While I, Ragini and Shubhra whiled away most of our time, the Maa Gos had done exactly what the senior had instructed me to do for an A-only, stopped taking bath, skipped combing and crammed, crammed and crammed more.

A week before the end-sems, the open question paper was distributed. Ragini and I looked at each other with eyes widened till eternity "Is he kidding? All in a week?"

It was an open question just for the heck of it. In each of the subject papers, there were as many as 25 questions covering the entire course. We were supposed to prepare all.

Three of us froze as Bahuguna declared. "In the end-sems, you would be asked to write any four answers."

"No choice, Sir?" Someone mustered up the courage.

"No choice, *beta*." None of the bargaining skills worked here though.

With entire syllabus covered and no choice in questions, this open question system was more of a trap to force students to prepare everything.

Ragini called an urgent General Body Meeting. All this while, Shubhra remained undisturbed. The GBM consensually agreed that I was to shift to the hostel with both of them.

I followed our decision, shifted to the hostel. The room was small and dingy, a glorified cubby hole which already seemed crowded with three full grown adults: Ragini, Shubhra and their third roommate Akriti. Another short girl, Ananya who for all purposes lived in the boys' wing was a semi- roomie who used to knock at 4 O'clock everyday, both morning and night.

She, it seemed, studied for the whole night in the boys' wing and in the wee hours of morning, knocked, slipped in and the four of us sleeping there had to contract our bodies a little further to accommodate another member on the bed.

Another GBM charted out our first strategy – beg for notes, forget all our ego, self respect. With Shubhra least bothered about the exams, it had to be Ragini and me who went from door-to-door begging for notes and crammed whatever bits and pieces of answer that our classmates threw at us like grand favours.

But two things need special mention here.

First, I almost felt certain that Shubhra, who had not touched any book as yet, was going to be the one to break the record and become the first one to get a 'C only'. Second, Adhbhut, under the pressure of civil services had taken a *Maunvrat* (vow of silence) and ran to bite whosoever went close to him. In short, Adhbhut and the three of us were not on talking terms anymore. The instant bond had turned soggy like frozen instant noodles.

Well it was two days to go for end-sem and yet we couldn't manage any answer for the first paper. Meanwhile rumours were doing rounds that the Maa Go club had managed to guess and reconstruct the question paper from the very early days of first-sem with help of senior Maa Go members (based on previous year question papers) and was very well prepared for the end-sem, a secret well preserved in a tight jar that leaked very late for us.

Our perspiration and palpitation knew no bounds. All this while, Shubhra stayed unperturbed. Emergency was declared in room no. 101, Tapti. Slogan was coined – Do or Die – followed by the third GBM where the final strategy was chalked out. I and Ragini were to attack Pinaki's room with sorry faces. Ragini was better at the sorry face. So she was to lead the squad which consisted of me and her.

We were to manage at least three answers from him for the first paper.

As the squad marched towards the final battle ground, the leader turned back and gave the final command "If need be, don't hesitate to use nuclear weapons. Those are your tears, but only if the need arises."

Knock Knock.

A reluctant Pinaki from inside the room "*Arrey*, who is it?" Sounding irritated to be disturbed two days before the exam, he was obviously in the race for A-only.

He was not happy to see our faces but before he could give us a polite excuse we had already barged in and made ourselves comfortable. Ragini began "Pinaki can you please help us understand the Comparative Advantage theory?"

Pinaki's uncombed hair, unintended spikes on scalp, unshaven face and dirty clothes made him a strong contender for an A-only. He took out the red and yellow 290 page *Bittoo* brand register and opened. We froze again on our seats. He had made colourful structured good looking notes for every answer; he opened the Comparative Advantage theory in which the diagram at that desperate moment appeared no less precious than Leonardo's masterpiece Monalisa.

Ragini and I exchanged glances but hardly communicated anything through them. Pinaki went on throwing light on different aspects of theory. It sounded like Hebrew then because our minds were racing fast to plan an acquisition or more appropriately a robbery.

After he finished, Ragini pleaded "Pinaki, can you do me a favour? Can I take this register, for something like, half an hour? I mean, I will read this again and return."

Pinaki was in a fix but could not somehow conjure up the right words to refuse though he warned tight "Not a minute more, *baba*." Once she caught hold of the register, Ragini's expression resembled that of a cat that who just pounced on its mouse.

We came back to the den, Tapti 101. Ragini started "What say, shall we?" I knew what she was talking about, I too shed all shame.

"Yeah let's do it."

Shubhra raised a feeble protest which was suppressed by the two warriors who had just won a battle. We rushed to Kamal Complex market, photocopied the entire register. While Ragini went with the conquest, hefty 290 paged ill stapled photocopy I, handed over the original register to the innocent victim.

Once photocopied, we already felt victorious as if we had managed an A-only in at least one of the papers. We celebrated by cheering our coffee which we prepared on the illegally hidden stove in the room. There was just a day left for the exam, when we realized that how much ever we crammed, it was impossible to cover the entire register. Besides it seemed too expensive to photocopy three sets, there was just one copy of the register. As a result, only one person could read one answer at a time.

So we decided to prepare selective questions and the questions were distributed. Ragini had the first pick by virtue of being the mastermind, executor and the leader. I chose my set of answers next as I was the assistant. The leftover for Shubhra continued to lie as and where they were. She had consciously decided to flunk. The day before the exam, Shubhra made coffee every hour so that all of us could stay awake all night. But the caffeine worked like Calmpose for me. Ragini crammed as much as she was capable of rocking on the chair to and fro.

D-day had arrived. The exam was to be of three hours, with a one hour break, followed by a practical exam of another three hours.

As the question paper was handed out, all the caffeine I consumed the night before started working. Out of the four questions marked, I had prepared just two. I looked at Ragini who looked back smilingly dangling at me her question paper. Oh God! She had got all the four questions she prepared. I did not care to look at Shubhra for she hadn't prepared any.

I spent 2 hours 15 minutes writing , beautifying the two answers I knew well. While attempting the rest, I deliberately scrawled illegibilly and made my handwriting complex in the hope that the Prof. assumes 'the poor fellow knew the answer but could not write for the lack of time.'

What was over was over. None of us really bothered to ask each other about our performances. The one hour break we spent in the canteen. Pinaki ordered for '*cheeken curry*' and why not, he deserved it every bit. I repented over mixed veg and dry chappatis.' 'I commited an immoral act by stealing Pinaki's answer, that is why God punished me.' Pat popped another thought. 'But God didn't punish Ragini!?'

Joy coolly finished his chicken curry and wiped his hands on his jeans, which he wore for the next three exams.

After the next three hours of draining practicals, the caffeine within me gave up. I collapsed. A triumphant Ragini mulled over next plan.

The most studious of the Maa Go group, Engli, lived in the same hostel, same floor and her window was bang opposite ours. Ragini kept a 24x7 watch. "Whenever she goes to the loo, we can just rush into her room for a quick check for all study materials for the next paper. If caught, we will pretend to have arrived just by chance."

After that day's disaster I was not enthusiastic, but again I reconsidered the guilt "If I don't have the answers, God anyway can't help me. So why not give it a try."

After five hours of constant vigil, the opportune moment arrived.

Ragini stroked me out of slumber and we ran. Midway through the run, when my gaze slipped to floor, I saw I was wearing two different slippers, but there was no time to return and change. When we peeped in, the room was full of papers. We urgently checked them out. They were too detailed readings, not of our use. No readymade stuff. The plan had failed. Accepting defeat, just when we turned to tip-toe out of the room, Engli entered with a big bunch of notes clutched in her hand. 'Oh my God, she actually carries her answers to the loo.'

She greeted disguising astonishment "Oh Hi! Come in, come in. I mean I will come in now that you are already in." She was courteous enough to offer us from her exam time biscuit stock and her body odour conveyed that she had been skipping bath for quite some time 'Oh God! Another serious contender for A-only.'

In front of us she put a key into her locked drawer, placed the books and bunch of notes inside and pulled out another bunch carefully locking it back.

'Ok, I think she had an inkling of the burglars in the hostel.' Whatever we quizzed her about, she let us know how she was not preparing that question for the exam.

So we realised that this was a lost cause, the prey was smarter than the hunter. After quickly excusing ourselves, we returned hopeless with hung heads.

Ragini and I prepared only the seven answers that we had, taking turns. Shubhra happily-merrily made coffee for us filling the vaccum of parent caring in hostel. Five of us fitted into Tapti's cramped room like Bollywood bombshells fit into their bustiers.

The second exam turned out to be worse for me and somewhere inside a rejected belief got about divine interventions got reinstated.

I knew only one question of the four and looked in despair towards my left. Ragini had hit bull's eye again, she showed me a thumbs up, I returned a thumbs down and couldn't suppress my disbelief and jealousy at that moment.

Since I had a lot of time, I practiced my neck-stretch exercises, I peeped towards my right and left. What I saw on my right threw me off my seat. Arpita Shekhawat had comfortably placed her register in the holder below her bench sporting a very calm-*Budhha* look over the bench. She filled pages after pages. A sincere and composed student drowned in her answer sheet, much of the activities were however concentrated under the table, much like stories that unfold in the Govt offices. So two different stories were shaping up simultaneously. One above the table, one below it. My first impulse was to complain 'Ma'am she is cheating' At least that way I could spoil another person's exam but then I suppressed the urge convincing myself that it would be a juvenile move. Instead I concocted many stories that day on my answer sheet, did full justice to my creative juices.

After practicals we strolled back and sat for a few minutes in the Tapti reception. I noticed then that the attendants went into a room turn by turn and shut the room from inside. I asked Pinaki casually "What's that room meant for?"

He shook his head. "I don't know."

I spoke aloud. "I think it's a loo." He did not seem to agree. "A loo in November? Are you mad or what. Delhi only has loo in May."

He had mistaken bathroom for the duststorm in summer which is locally called loo in India.

I concluded he was too well prepared for the next paper '*Regional Geography of India*'.

On that night the semi-roomie Ananya came back early from the boy's hostel taking all of us by surprise. It was not yet her time to return "What happened Ananya? No studies today?" I spoke to lighten the atmosphere that had grown heavy with the overloaded room.

"Today Jitesh, Vibhu and Sambit are not studying. They are watching those kind of movies on their computer."

I cleared the concept "The XXX types"

"And they told you to buzz off?"

"Yes, they asked me to come back tomorrow." Then she recounted us names of the cheesy favourites among triple X-rated movies.

On the day of the third exam we bumped into Adhbhut early morning. He gave us a royal ignore and we returned the treatment by making disgusting faces.

Once the question papers were handed over, for the first time I felt relieved at my good hit rate. Three out of four were prepared questions. When I ritually threw a glance at Ragini, her face had bloated like a swollen potato. She showed me her question paper.

She hadn't managed to get even one question from her prepared list. I felt sad for her but somewhere deep down, I also knew relief. At least I have always been in a better position than that. I looked at my right side. Arpita, smart girl, was busy copying from her register with unprecedented expertise. Practice makes the skill perfect.

I didn't care. I knew three-fourth of the paper today. In the middle of exam I pitifully threw a glance at Ragini. Poor girl, she was scribbling hard. 'When you don't know what to write, you tend to write more. When you know that quality is suffering you try to compensate by quantity.' I sympathized.

After the exam, I patted Ragini, "For questions that you didn't know anything about, you managed to write more than decently."

"Oh! That paper? Thank God I escaped."

"Meaning?"

"Meaning, Adhbhut was sitting next to me. After I went through my question paper I didn't know what to do, so I was helplessly looking here and there. That was when my eyes scanned Adhbhut's paper. His paper had all the four question I had prepared but he seemed glum. I quietly showed him my paper and suddenly his eyes lit up with greed. We didn't waste time and exchanged our question papers."

"But we are not talking to him!"

"So what? I still didn't talk to him nor do I intend to."

"My God! Some people have all the luck in the world." I thought.

The very next day was my last exam. But then Ragini's friend's brother's friend had dropped by to pile on Ragini and Shubhra for a fortnight.

It was then that I decided 'No this is not working for any of us. It is getting more crowded than a Nazi camp.' So I headed straight for home.

At home I crammed through the only four answers I had at my disposal. For once, devoid of other distraction-disturbance I seriously studied the entire night and when it struck four in the clock, the sleepy dawn possessed me and I gave up. I lied down on the little space on my bed which now had a mattress of loose papers everywhere, fixing the alarm for six.

At 6.10, I woke up with a strange blocked ear feeling. I couldn't yet figure out whether it was cold or something else that led to this indescribable excruciating pain in my ear. During those anxious moments, my ear tasted warm mustard oil and a concoction of all kinds of ear drops available at home, apart from being searched thoroughly by ear buds for some clue.

But nothing seemed to help and as my parents took an appointment with an ENT specialist for the evening (how on earth could I miss my exams?), I headed for JNU.

However, by the time I reached the class, the pain just got worse. I went to the Professor concerned and narrated my problem. She was considerate enough to let me give the exam the next day, and I headed straight for the Emergency Dept of RML hospital.

In the hospital, as the doc examined my affected ear, he got the shock of his life. Before I could figure out what exactly had transpired, he excitedly screamed out to all his colleagues. With several faces staring right down at my ear, I felt nothing less than a guinea pig on trial. Well, it was then my turn to shriek when he poked the forceps into my ear to pull out a small cockroach (still huge for the ear) neatly split into two halves. He fitted two parts of the jig-saw-puzzle and placed the slain cockroach on a fluffy cotton for exhibition.

I couldn't take any more liberties with the exam. The next day, encashing on one extra day I had gone prepared with 16 out of 21 questions, a record in itself. But, my luck being my luck and not Ragini's, I again found only two prepared questions out of four.

Rubbish, the end sem was over and we had learnt our lessons.

Finally when the grade points were declared

1. Ragini and I had made into the bracket slot which we had selected for ourselves.

2. Pinaki too belonged to our slot. (His company made our slot respectable)

3. Two Maa Go members had predictably shot into A-only club.

4. Copycat-Arpita Shekhawat had also managed to crack into A-only club.

5. And believe it or not, the only other person who had rocketed into the distinguished A-only ranks was none other than our Shubhra.

After our experience in CSODR, we say our alphabets in a slightly changed sequence- A plus, A only, A minus, B plus, B only, B minus .....

5

Ganga Dhaba – The Intellectual Hotspot

Ganga Dhaba, the baby which JNU carried in its womb has grown up, on the refined-oil paranthas, to become an entity with its own distinct personality.

Analogically, Paranthewali gali procreated by Chandni Chowk fed on desi ghee paranthas, grew up to create its own robust identity.

Just as parents affectionately gaze at their successful children, JNU feels proud of Ganga Dhaba which had carved out a place for itself amongst Delhi's interesting hang outs.

Ganga Dhaba (GD) is the nocturnal hotspot of JNU. JNU's active social nightlife is centered around GD. One can safely name GD the parantha pub. Parantha because that is the cheapest and perpetual attraction of GD. Pub to impart the glamour and style it deserves and intoxicating effect it produces.

Its intoxicating effect is felt mainly by lovers who see their beloved in dim, filtered, neon streetlights which conceal most flaws. This was precisely why most of the love stories that began in GD did not last long.

As the day breaks, the scorching sun reveals hidden realities like moles, scars and many wonder, "Is she the same girl I was flirting with last night!"

When the clock strikes 11 and most Delhites slip into their comfy night suits, it is time for JNU, or better still GD visitors to dress up. About 11.30, many nice girls in JNU receive calls from their parents whom they dutifully promise that they would study harder. On the phones they yawn a few times to signal to their parents that it is already bed-time for them and that their goody-goody daughter is going to hit the bed in a second from now.

While parents feel relieved and dispel doubts that their daughter has not fallen into bad company, the daughters give finishing touches to their makeup.

When it strikes 12, Ganga Dhaba is full of hustle and bustle, where you will spot all nice girls who were faking yawns till a few minutes back.

GD has never been the official dating spot of JNU. It never made its money from lovers. However, the section GD targets is "would be lovers". In a way it is the official pre-dating destination of JNU.

Guys and girls spend months in GD before their love blooms and is formalized. But what happens after that is no mystery, at least not in JNU.

A guy or girl frequenting GD on a daily basis implies clear signs of a "falling in love syndrome". Till s/he is religiously dressing up for the night, you can bet that one is still on the trying mode. If a certain somebody disappears after a long stint at GD, there is high probability s/he has given up on love. However if two individuals in most cases, of opposite sex, evaporate from the scene at the same time, then you can safely infer that two trying modes have culminated into an affair and hence shifted from the noisy hotspot to a quiet love spot or boyfriend's hostel room.

GD is the Page 3 of JNU and for the lack of an uniting festival this compensates as a socializing arena where inter-Centre and inter-hostel bonds are built and strengthened.

However these are not the reasons why GD is famous outside JNU. It is better known for the hot political debates, soaked in passion, a quest for an alternative model of development, which triggered noises (Oh sorry, 'voices' would be more appropriate) that found an echo in the Parliament Building.

Well those debates if not extinct, have definitely gained the status of an artefact on its way to museum. Generation X is smarter in every walk of life, so why should JNU be any different? This generation has learnt vicariously from the previous generations' mistake. It has seen a few of those hot debaters leading a life shrouded with anonymity and insignificance, having a tough time, even fending for their families. Well, Gen-X has also heard through the folk oral tradition, the stories of how those who debated once with their heart and souls, have been shot dead in feudal political rivalries and forced to be martyrs. Those who lived on are dying of hunger anyway. That explains the reduced political activity in JNU. This sense of detachment from politics is consciously cultivated.

For this I must congratulate my comrades. Bravo, for history is witness to the fact that individual heroic actions have never ever solved national problems. However, coming back to GD, if not hot political debates then what keeps the spot still throbbing is anybody's guess.

The conversations today conform to the contemporary development paradigm.

As Amartya Sen puts it "Development is about enlarging people's choices." On the same lines, a night at GD offers you choice of joining any conversation that suits your general temperament or prevailing mood.

The amalgamation of global politics with local campus politics, frivolous talks ranging from geography of girl's anatomy to great philosophical moorings, future plans of self to fate of the nation, all of this served with the refined oil parantha and chai.

On offer here is a sample taste of the exhaustive menu that is a little bit....oh! sorry...a small bite from few selected dish.

As I, Rag and Shubhra perched ourselves on the rocks that serve as seats in Ganga Dhaba, I began in right earnest on what I meant to do. I eavesdropped in every possible direction my ears permitted me to.

The view was of Khadi Kurtas lamenting over rising smoke, both of which have become symbols of gender equality in JNU. Khadi Kurta, signifying the highest level of unisex dressing, much higher than trousers which originally belonged to men but have been adopted by women and the smoke that in JNU is considered less of a fashion statement, more a path to intellectual elevation (God knows why). So guys and girls smoke in small groups in GD pondering over following:

To my **North East:**

They were planning to protest against the US president in the wake of Iraq War.

X: So here we finalize that effigy of George Bush is to be burnt at 6 O'clock tomorrow, in the Kendriya Vidyalaya grounds.

Y: But comrade, why did you not accept Chitra's cartoon of George Bush? She had spent two days making it, worked hard on it and now she is very upset, almost inconsolable.

X: Come on, her cartoon looked more like Saddam Hussain with those fluffy cheeks and broad nose. I asked her to draw another cutout with big ears. What if people mistake our campaign to be against Saddam instead of Bush?

Z: It is just a symbol comrade, you don't have to take it so seriously. If we are shouting slogans against Bush, we must be burning Bush's effigy only.

Y : And let me tell you, Chitra and her friends will not give any old clothes to make a Bush's puppet the way you have planned, a stuffed toy effigy. Not after her cutout has been rejected.

To my **North West** :

Only-boys club conducting beauty contest.

A : Whatever you say, Rohini's TRP* rating is No.1 in Tapti hostel.

B : Just because her side profile resembles Kareena Kapoor, you are flat over her. She cannot beat Ashima. Most of the guys in my row have started waking up early for breakfast so that they can catch a glimpse of Ashima's breathtaking fresh morning beauty. Ashima is an early riser, she goes jogging exactly at 5:30, back to hostel by 6:30, in the mess for breakfast by 7:30 dot.

C : Just don't get personal about the TRP ratings. If you guys

---

*TRP - Total Rating Points.

just put your love interests on top TRP ratings, the whole process will lose meaning. The TRP rating in any hostel must operate on a consensus and every aspect of beauty must be thoroughly examined in detail before the final verdict is passed.

To my **South West:**

Another political affiliation is planning a destructive act.

M : Listen you guys, today our final appeal to cancel the non-veg dinner on this Wednesday has been rejected by the mess secretary.

(JNU hostels have fixed days in a week on which non-veg is served in the mess)

N : How can he be so insensitive to the majority opinion?

O: It is *Maha-shivaratri* and he himself is a Hindu. How can we eat veg from the same kitchen where non-veg is cooked on this auspicious day? *Saala..m**** dharambhrasht karaega.*

N : Action must be taken. So, what do you say, what should be the plan of action now?

M : I have chalked out a strategy but the party fund should sponsor it.

O : I am the treasurer, *saala* I will help pass the bill. You *saala* just brief us on your plan.

M : Our party members, even from other hostels, should queue up from 7 O' Clock as a protest and cut dinner coupons for all the non-veg thalis. Dinner time starts at 7.30 PM. By then we should already stand in the queue with plates, buy all the non-veg thalis and destroy the food by throwing it into the bin.

O : Good, that will *saala* make news also. Bigger news than the torch protest of those comrades *saala*.

To my **South East:**

A few guys discussing career options.

U : This was your final attempt.

V : In civil services? No, it was my third but what difference does it make anyway. After a year both of us will be seated on some other rocks in the same place and I would be telling you that it was my last attempt and I still did not make it.

U : Very dicey yaar, what about your girlfriend that Shibani alias Tumpa?

V : When you fail, everyone leaves. The first year of your exam everyone is enthusiastic about you, the second year they support you, the third year, all those who supported you once, look the other way. By the final year, you are all alone, just concluding something formally, that you started way back.

U : This five-year plan sounds worse than the Govt.'s five year plan.

V : Once you are in JNU, you either go the Massachusetts way or the Munirka way and sadly I am on the Munirka way.

Let me tell all those faceless Kurtas that only they, who have seen the pain and struggle in life so closely, would be able to value and enjoy success as and when it comes. These conversations inspire me to philosophize on the question: why GD remains the throbbing heart of JNU and why Nilgiri Dhaba, Sabarmati Dhaba could never kick Ganga Dhaba out of business?

Since I have already promised a philosophical answer, I cannot forward arguments like an historical inertia of the place or the like.

The philosophical explanation I can put forward:

Like the heart is not located in the geometrical centre of the body but still holds its importance over other lowly organs, Ganga Dhaba is not located in the centre of JNU. It is in fact very close to the main North Gate which is the way out from JNU.

This spot is in a way the closest interface with the outer world by virtue of being physically closer to North gate. The North gate exhales frustrated unemployed air and inhales fresh air from outside. This spot is also not yet the outer world itself which is relatively exorbitantly expensive, which still measures young men's success not by their knowledge but the fatness of their salaries and we JNUites do not fully feel comfortable and worthwhile in such environment.

Therefore, we prefer to meet in the horizon where the outer world meets the inner world to celebrate our knowledge and to console our poverty.

This description of Ganga Dhaba will be truly belied if you choose to visit this historical location in broad daylight. For then it wears a desolate, deserted look with no grand construction waiting for you. That makes us realize that no amount of concrete structure, architectural magnificence can substitute for the people who impart the flavour of the place that it is. For what would be Kolkata without Bengalis, Patna without Biharis, and JNU without all of them and more.

6

Parthasarathy Rocks

If Ganga Dhaba is the official pre-dating destination of JNU, Parthasarathy Rocks (PSR) is undoubtedly the official dating spot. Once couples sign the agreement of love, they most definitely visit the love shrine of PSR and, with the blessings of Lord PS proceed on the path of love.

Far from the madding crowd, right under the gaze of the first Vice Chancellor (G. Parthasarathy) of JNU, they explore the lanes of love, dark and lighted with herds of mosquitoes, insects of all types, porcupine, neelgai, and obviously the rocks.

The rocks are like the three good monkeys of Gandhiji with shut mouth, closed eyes and blocked ears. Believe me, rocks are better confidants than your best friends for never has it happened that Parthasarathy Rocks have let out a secret in any weak tempting moment. Though I won't be shocked to death if the rocks do gossip amongst themselves about the steamy scenes they witness in some code language of silence.

PSR is a beautiful scenic place, where relics of Aravali declare that their territory is over after this point. They bow out finally after a long marathon which they started in the western edge of India.

JNU is one of the rare areas in the crowded capital of India, where you get the luxury of walking 20 minutes and feeling as if you are already amidst woods.

But amongst the JNU *junta* the connotation of PSR is slightly different. Those who visit PSR in dark nights for obvious reason do not inform in the mornings that they did so. A few of those who actually go there for rather innocent reasons and foolishly spill the beans the following morning get a prompt question back "In whose arms?"

The first Vice Chancellor of JNU must be shedding tears. While it is a great privilege for anyone to have a place named after himself, it might not be one of his greatest wishes that a place which is not known for the right reason carries his name.

For God's sake the authorities could have picked up a better place to bear his name. For instance the administration building or the nine storey stone library building or for that matter the open air theatre.

Mr. Parathasarathy looks the other way as PSR bears with a heavy heart the smaller vices of this society. By smaller vices I mean nobody commits murder or attempts rape there. The witness to what happened the previous night at PSR are the littered used condoms, empty Mc Dowells No. 1 bottles and doping residues. PSR bears the consequences of the three sure shot ways to the altered state of consciousness.

1. Doping

2. Drinking

3. Making love

It has produced many an Aristotle and Plato who themselves forgot the next morning that they actually propounded theories with such profound philosophy in their sense of *déjà vu*.

An intruding peep into the private world of dopers, drinkers and lovers, when they were in their trance.

The trance of Mc Dowells

Curly hair: Is it a sin to love....hic... somebody your mother's age?

Pony tail: No friend, love can never be a sin. Love can just be....hmm...see how I don't know what love is?

Bald patch: Sin is conscious, love is unconscious. Sin is deliberate, love is unintentional. You don't apply for love, you just fall in love.

Pony tail: Bloody why do you always.....hic...fall in love? Why can't you rise in it?

Curly hair: Boss, in India you can never rise in love. First, the girl's parents will bash you up. And whatever little is left of you will be finished off by your own parents' beatings...so....so...so.. you can never rise. But I still love the old woman. Why is it a sin to love your Prof.? But you guys, you swear on your mom first, that you'll not tell this to anyone that...that...I sinned in loving my old Prof.

Bald patch (stood up): Age, my friend, is nothing but a fallacy of mind. It is a dynamic concept...hic...like time, it doesn't stay still. Your age doesn't wait, it grows older and older till the full stop of your life. Once you are dead, your age stops right there. When your dad dies at 80, he never turns 81. And if you die at 81...your age then is one year older than your dad. So there, your Prof. will die one day and stop growing older after that. But you will still grow my friend till you reach her age and you too die. That is your moment...hic...to propose to her.

Curly hair: (No response, must have passed out)

Pony tail: ... (No response, must have passed out as well)

The trance of grass/dope

Brown Kurta: Why did I come here? To see this day? I promised my parents...I'll become an IAS one day.

Green Kurta: Chill son chill! Imagine that all of us are in heaven.

Brown Kurta: Final attempt is over. IAS, my foot. I don't even have a clerk's job. And hell, over that I am doping here.

Green Kurta: Chill out son. Success is elusive, success is an illusion, a mirage. Don't run after it. See we are flying over the ninth floor of library. Enjoy the ride.

Brown Kurta: Bloody sucker Adhbhut. He made it. And that Jignesh, how could he, how could he make it? Oh God! Why man why?

Blue Kurta: Son, this place is the cremation ground of your dreams. Thousands of dreams are cremated here every year, you are no special. Life is full of sorrow son. Struggle is the purpose of life...we are born by struggle, of struggle and to struggle. Think of those two organisms who struggled to conceive, think of that one sperm who struggled, competed with millions of other sperms to become a foetus. We are born out of that struggle and to struggle.

Green Kurta : Chill son chill, are you flying with me now...over UPSC?

Brown Kurta: Yes I am flying.

Blue Kurta: And how do you feel on your first flight to heaven?

Brown Kurta: I feel ... I think .....No I am not sure, but I think I am becoming an IAS.

The trance of love

Where boulders double up as the mattress and rock act as pillows and lovers lie down uncomfortably on the uneven terrain. The guy at 65 degree and the girl at 75 degree.

Guy: Darling this is the most ecstatic moment of my life.

Girl: Really? Mine too, just minus the fears.

Boy: What fears honey?

Girl: What not, dear? Fear of being caught by some slimy men in the midst of the act, fear of being bitten by a snake while you are making out. Are there bigger fears in the world than these? Just take your teeth off my thighs.

Guy: Thigh! My face is near your stomach honey.

Girl's: Liar, liar. Don't get naughty.

For the following of the three-four days, she caressed the insect bite on her thigh mistaking it to be a love bite.

The peaceful ambience of PSR was disturbed by a bunch of goons. While the lovers, drinkers and dopers reached the 'Aha' peak experience, a mob of CSODR-ians were planning to break their harmony by holding bonfire in the midst of PSR. They seemed all prepared to shake and wake

1) The Dopers

2) The Drinkers

3) The Lovers

4) The Nature

In CSODR division of labour was carried out. Two groups of guys were sent out to buy kerosene oil and logs of wood from Munirka and Katwaria Sarai respectively. Some of us went about exploring the site and collecting supply of extra wood to prolong the burning fire.

As the dusk dimmed into darkness, we all started walking towards PSR. After a few bonfire specialists created the ambience, all of us settled down with a filmy atmosphere engulfing us. A few minutes from then and an eerie silence set in. Suddenly no one knew what to say or what to do. We all sat there feeling stupid and looking at the fire as if it were performing an item number.

The silence was growing awkward when one of the guys coaxed another to recite a few *sher* (verse). That was that. As if he was waiting for an opportune invitation to start. In his artificially created pensive voice he bored us to death.

> *"tumko dekha toh yeh khayal aaya,*
> *tumko dekha toh yeh khayal aaya,*
> *tumko dekha, tumko dekha*
> *toh yeh khayal aaya,*
> *zindagi dhoop hum ghana saaya"*

In the name of original *sher*, he went on reciting bollywood songs one after another. He was rechristened "*Dard*" (pain) from that day onwards.

Dard's baptising ceremony set the tone for fun. This Dard had two connotations, one for the guy himself who was made to believe that this name rightly signifies the depth and pain that his heart and soul is soaked in. The other connotation was for rest of us, meaning what a pain this guy was for us to tolerate. From then on, he was openly mocked at while he did his best to live up to the name and profound persona by buying cheap Hindi *shero-shairi* second hand books from the footpath near Priya.

We revisited the bonfire site many times over. Sometimes, we played archaeologists, trying to give meanings to mundane things there. We studied and tried to rebuild history by discovering names carved out on the thick barks of the trees and rocks. Sahil loves Archana. Vivek + Ruchika. Many love birds had encased themselves in a shape of heart, a shape that still comes free in today's times, when everything from water to sex costs a fortune in the market.

As the saying goes these lovebirds in their peak experience must have carved out their own names. As their love tenure ended, they went ahead, got married to more convenient partners. They recognized the other name on the rock with awkward expression whenever the two names bumped into each other.

In PSR love is in the air and our bonfires proved it. As all of us went screaming singing our hearts out, living our youth to the maxim, some things were changing.

As the fire was set ablaze, sitting positions around it gradually changed, throwing signals of who liked whom, who avoided whom and which of us had reached some clandestine understanding.

During our initial trips to PSR, most of us would cling together for the fear of having to say 'hi' to a stray wolf. Now, a few times old in the place, though we started together and enjoyed through the bonfire in unison, on our way back from the site, many disappeared into the woods like ghosts. God knows, which path of trance they chose.

While we had established our Kingdom in the dark, the displaced and disturbed were not sitting idle. They conspired back.

Once after our regular merrymaking sessions, we were just back when we saw the message awaiting us "The CSODR Chairperson wants to meet MA first semester urgently. Report at Committee Room at 10.00 A.M. sharp."

The next day as we walked to the Centre wondering what the special occasion was, we encountered the disturbed and the displaced under the guise of an environment friendly group; a bunch of students dressed in green with green banners stood boycotting us.

As we walked straight up to the committee room, the Chairperson fumed at us "In the morning you study ecological conservation techniques and at night, you go and pollute the environment, wasting wood. These are not the values we give you here at CSODR. This is the last warning for you. If you carry on this menace, all of you will get an F in the ecology paper. Now go back to your classes."

Our bonfire sessions ended abruptly but meanwhile many from our class had joined the old PSR clubs, those of dopers, drinkers and lovers who coexisted in amity and harmony. The old Kingdom at PSR was reinstated. Parthasarathy rocks smiled back and embraced its old friends.

On second thoughts, I think there could be no other place in JNU more meaningful than PSR to have been named after the first VC. The PSR rocks are most intellectual of the rock species, for they patiently listen to the academics, theorists and thinkers in the dark, who propound deep philosophies without expecting any awards. These rocks also remain quiet witnesses to the many promises and oaths that lovers make and break. They have absorbed many tears after those promises were broken and oaths forgotten. These rocks love the dopers, drinkers and lovers and that is the reason that they refuse to budge from their places since so many years.

7

Salwar Kurtas to UGs

There is a theory waiting to be propounded on female dressing in JNU. The plebian version of the theory in unacademic words goes like this.

Girls who enter JNU in jeans generally spend their postgraduation days in the same, though gracefully they add a few salwar kurtas in their wardrobe. Women who enter JNU in salwar kurtas, in most likelihood, take to jeans sooner than later. A raid into the wardrobe of a JNU woman of substance will display a range of T-shirts, salwar, kurtas, skirts, jeans and baby kurtas called kurtis. All of these she wears in permutation and combination except one combo i.e. salwar with T-shirt which still has not struck any super-imaginative mind of our fashion designers and hence remains out of vogue.

Now that I have floated the idea, I expect the ever inspired fashion brigade of our country to take a cue. Apart from the above, a few girls, who entered JNU in ill-fitting nylon terycot synthetic kurtas also transform and metamorphose into something else. This variety is an exotic species on the campus. Initially you do not notice them in the crowd but one day when you do notice them, you crinkle your eyes, hoping that the act would make the blurred picture a little clearer. Then you discover you were right in recognizing the nylon-tericot girls, only that somethings have changed.

The caterpillars have indeed evolved into butterflies, only not the colourful ones that you spot in the domestic gardens but the wild ones, browns and greys who startle, shock and scare you at the same time.

In the dreadful winter of Delhi, when cats and dogs (who kind of have a birthright to roam naked royally) die to wear woollens, the nylon-tericot variety decides to do some charity......provide relief to starving lusty eyes by shedding some clothes.

The scene that startled, shocked and scared you were the legs that always existed behind the nylon salwars, but you never noticed, now stood fully exposed. The only fabric clinging were the tiny cycling shorts – shiny, stretchable, thigh hugging – teamed with Sarojini Nagar export market undersized tops (they never fit right, not even accidentally, they have to be either over-sized or under-sized).

Whoops! A hundred questions pop up in your mind as if it were a popcorn making machine with just the optimal temperature 'when, how and why did this happen...this makeover'.

May be these nylon tericot variety had taken the professors too seriously and literally who had oft repeated the quote "There is no point being unnecessarily lengthy. Whatever statements you make should be brief, crisp and appealing. Nobody in the busy world has time to pay attention to your statements – they should be different, catchy so that they capture the concerned person's attention automatically."

Looks like while the professor made that comment about

statements in your answer-sheets, the nylon-tericot variety had generalized its application to include all sorts of statements including the fashion statements they made.

Here, we concern ourselves with the evolution of two such characters right in my class who had eventually become very high scorers on òomphometers.

One of them was from Midnapore, the other one from Lakhisarai. They were not exactly impressive when I first met them.

Rewind to First semester. Play.

About the ninth or tenth day of the semester, I entered the class all alone as Rag was mourning her fish CB's death anniversary (one of her usual *bahanas* to miss class). I had reached a little early for except me there were just two other fellows. I noticed that in an empty class, two plump women huddled together in one corner very close to each other.

I walked up to them and as we exchanged introduction, I got a chance to see them from close quarters, and quite carefully.

Both of them definitely belonged to the nylon-terricot variety. One of them had a face so symmetrically round, as if drawn with a compass. The other one's face was so oval that it could pass off as humpty-dumpty-egg head. Their hair looked as if they had been too generous with the oil, tightly plaited. Their faces looked greasy, size of their specs too big for their faces and their lips shone like mirror out of extra bit of Vaseline that they had smeared.

In brief, except for the shape of their heads, they looked like Siamese twins. Let's call them Itsy and Bitsy. Itsy had a very nervous voice. Bitsy had no voice at all (or so it seemed then) because she didn't speak, just smiled at whatever I had to say, even at the most mundane things like "In Delhi it gets really cold by mid-November." Can't tell you how I exactly felt about Itsy and Bitsy because I never spared a thought about the twosome after that meeting. I mean they hardly made an impression to command an afterthought.

However very soon I did get a chance to form a common opinion on those two. Once when I was dozing off in Tapti 101, I realized that apart from the five of us, two of Rag's long lost friends dropped by unannounced to spend the night over in JNU. The air grew stale and claustrophobic; I mean seven in a room in Tapti was just impossible. Just sitting there with the other six was making me feel nauseous (the two new friends were chain smokers, icing on the cake). I made an excuse and went up to the terrace to get some fresh air.

As I looked onto the vacant space, somebody startled me by softly touching my shoulders from behind. I turned back to find Itsy. She sat besides me, as darkness grew dense, we had quite a heart to heart with each other. Post dinner, Bitsy came looking for Itsy and made herself comfortable next to us. Bitsy still didn't speak much. Itsy spoke on her behalf "These big town girls are so mean. Look at Bitsy's room mate. She is bossing around all the time. Yesterday she shouted at her so loudly that most of the hostel heard it."

"But why? I mean why did she shout?"

"Because Bitsy was completing her assignment so she kept the light on after 11 which her roommate found difficult to sleep with."

"That is so terrible yaar."

"And you know Bitsy's roommate sometimes makes her sleep on the floor, when her friend from Ganga hostel stays over for the night."

"Why don't you shout back at her, Bitsy? This is so clearly unfair."

"I don't know...she is older than me."

"But if you do not tell her anything, you will suffer for two years. She is your roomie *yaar*! Promise me that you'll speak up for yourself."

"I shall try."

Itsy spoke again "You know we do not have that kind of confidence, that smartness like you girls."

I felt touched "Hey why do you say so?"

Itsy continued "Really I mean it. When I see you talking to the boys in the class, you look so confident. But whenever a boy comes to talk to me, I feel something strange happening in my stomach."

I was puzzled "Why? You have something against the male species or what?"

Itsy had appointed me her counsellor "No, no. It is not like that. Just that my vocabulary dries up and words don't come to my mind anymore. It is not that I don't want to talk to them. Sometimes I really want to be friends with them. But at our place, it is not considered so good to have a boyfriend...err...I mean friends who are boys."

"It's all right Itsy. Don't worry. As time passes you'll have lots of friends who are boys. You are such a nice girl after all. I'll formally introduce you to guys in our class. That should make things easier for you."

I was moved by their simplicity and innocence.

"You are so sweet and sensitive. Both of us thought otherwise about you. You don't look the understanding type. We felt you must be quite snobbish but you are so comfortable to talk to....What is your zodiac sign?"

"Pisces."

Bitsy sounded excited "Mine too."

That night on the terrace, my heart went out to those two simple girls who were struggling to adjust to the fast life they were thrown into.

Itsy's nervous voice spoke after a little hesitation "Do you think…the three of us can be best friends?"

Thank God it was dark. I answered equally hesitant "Why not! All of us are best friends."

I knew I sounded stupid. I also knew I was lying but I just couldn't hurt them.

Fast forward to Second Sem. Play.

That night the promise made by three friends on terrace did not go futile. Two-third had complied, only one had back stepped and the traitor was your's truly. Likemindedness had ensured that Itsy and Bitsy were the inseparable Siamese twins. Though their friendship had not changed, their looks definitely had. Just as I had described the two of them in pretty much the same words initially, applying a similar technique would do here as well.

Their hair was still unkempt but with no trace of oil, remained dishevelled and frizzy, to the extent that I must confess that the oily plaits were much better.

Open frizzy hair went well with their blood red and vermilion red lipsticks their tongues licking-tasting the lipstick every now and then.

God, some accessorizing they were into. Two large *Raw Ban** branded goggle paired with jewels studded heels. They definitely followed the season's fashion trends for they had message printed

---

* Duplicates from Palika Market.

T shirts on (must be two sizes smaller than their actual size) most of the time. Only the messages went a little overboard. 'Am a hottie' and 'virgins don't last, the rest have a blast', worn with the latest fad jeans with what seemed like the entire Mughal garden embroidered on the denim with sequins that shone too brightly. Only when they displayed their bulging backs that one had this unstoppable urge to pull their T-shirts little further down to make it bearable for most of us. The view was of, as rightly described by Rag, 'divide and rule'. It was something that you so badly wanted to take your eyes off but could not.

Now this was the exotic species in JNU and they were bound to be noticed and mocked. I too joined the bandwagon of girls in my class. They were the laughing stock and we cracked jokes about them with as much meanness that girls of our age could have. But deep down somewhere, may be in just a square millimeter area in my heart, I longed to ask Itsy and Bitsy to use the full length mirror that was exclusively provided for in the girls wings of hostel.

But the twosome were on a different high. Itsy had caught a 'vanishing syndrome' which meant night after night she remained absconding and untraceable, nobody yet had any idea of where she disappeared. Bitsy had caught another flu 'the big word syndrome'. It was proving to be very tough for us. From the time when she never spoke because she was comfortable only in her mother tongue, she had come a long way. With her grammar all screwed up she didn't forget to use heavy words in her sentences.

I had a feeling she just picked up words from the dictionary in the morning and decided that she must use it anyhow on that very day. We noticed it first when she peeped into Tapti 101.

"Hello guys, do you have some mucilage (glue)? I want to implement some pasting on my term papers."

"AIDS. Scary quite a myxomatosis (contagious) disease."

"What to talk about sir. Yes he objurgates (scolds) in the class but at least he is munificent (generous) in giving grades."

Well rumours had it that Bitsy had fallen in love with a stud whom she had met in a chatroom over the internet. This cyberworld can be credited with fixing up a dog with a cat and a cat with a rat and a rat with a grain. He was a *pucca Jat* from Haryana and was now dating her. I wonder though how Bitsy communicated with him.

The other day Rag returned from Bitsy's room all scandalized. "Believe me Kaya she has written poems in English, which she herself professes to be love poems, but to me they sound simply porno yaar."

Itsy-Bitsy rocked but only for each other.

Fast forward to Third Sem, Play.
Itsy-Bitsy's necklines plunged and hemlines went up. Now their cellulite was for all the world to see.

But one day Rag returned from the common bathroom with a juicy piece of news that broke all records. Rumors had it that Itsy-Bitsy were doing free rounds in the hostel corridors with just their undergarments on.

"Now this is a bit too much to believe." I simply didn't agree.

"Come on why should Rumpa lie about it? I distinctly heard her. Infact turned off the shower so that sound could filter better."

"These girls…when they get bitchy…they can rip you apart in seconds. Character assassination is a favorite pass time in any girl's hostel."

"OK. As if we care. Let them roam in their briefs or no briefs." Rag ended the conversation.

Now these things spread faster than fire. I could just sense the hush-hush every where in Tapti. In the common toilet, the wash basin, pantry, TV room, terrace. There were whispers everywhere about these two girls who were wandering about the hostel in their lingerie.

Now JNU was liberal and it did give individual freedom to dress but that certainly did not mean "no dress." I still would not have believed it hundred per cent except for that day's accident when we had to deliver some urgent message to all the CSODR girls who lived in Tapti. So there, our trio knocked at Itsy's door.

"Come on in!"

As Rag banged the door open, we were done to shame. Two huge plump figurine spread in front of us. Itsy-Bitsy in their bare minimals. Their right hand clutched a glass with golden translucent liquid in it. It could be Appy Fizz, giving them the benefit of doubt. Their left hand was holding a cigarette in style.

The scene reminded me of a cheesy snap of Silk Smitha which I happened to accidentally bump into during my childhood. Even at that tender age, the image had shocked me enough to have persisted in my mind.

Bitsy, very matter of factly, pulled a cloth after a few seconds, finally she showed some mercy on us. "It is getting so hot in Delhi. We are just not used to this kind of heat back home."

'Yeah sure! You were born on Brazilian beaches to be blessed with such a dressing sense.' I thought to myself.

Three of us sat there in awkwardness. Like blinds, our gazes transfixed on single spots – Shubhra's gaze on her nails which rested on her own lap, my gaze on the poster which hung above Itsy's head and Rag's on Bitsy's assets.

"Good riddance." We blurted out as we did an escapado from there completely forgetting the urgent message that we had to pass on.

Fast Forward to Fourth sem. Play.

Now it was official. While bikes changed from *Splendor* to *CBZ* to *Karizma* and the riders changed too, the rear seats were reserved for Itsy and Bitsy. The new rumor was even more explosive. That one of them indulged in "orgy". I could neither confirm, nor deny it completely.

Once in the canteen when Rag was on one of her cribbing trips "See how I have gained on my arms, can't wear sleeveless any more, at least not this season", we had no idea that we were being eavesdropped.

Itsy, who was facing away from us on the other chair, turned back to lecture "Madam Rag, you are turning into a woman. Learn to live with those fats. They are signs that we are no more skinny teens. Believe me, men like those fats. Enjoy your womanhood."

Before Rag could react, Bitsy commented "But before that, close your T-shirt collar button, it is open and looking quite vulgar."

"For someone who roams in UGs herself, this is too much to say *yaar*." Rag whined in whispers.

"Forget it Rag, don't pay heed. There is no point getting into a catfight."I deprived the canteen fellow of some great action stuff.

After a few weeks that night Rag, Shubhra and I went to Priya Complex for our weekend movie quota.

Next day early in the morning, I started for home. I quietly slipped out of 101 so as not to make any noise to wake up anybody else and tip toed out of Tapti hostel. There I saw someone zigzagging, cat walking towards hostel almost off balance.

As the figure drew closer, I realized it was Itsy. I didn't quite understand the state she was in. Was she drunk? As she approached me, she completely lost balance and fell flat puking all over the road in front of the hostel. Now that was quite a scene. I instinctively ran to her to help. As I looked at her face, she seemed drowsy and exhausted. I helped her to her room from where Bitsy took over.

I returned to discover that her bag was lying orphan on the road, from which some receipts had fallen off. Presuming it could be important, I headed back towards her room to return the bag and those yellow receipts just when the papers caught my attention. Those bills belonged to a clinic in Vasant Kunj notorious for its illegal abortions.

I did not probe further, returned the bag to Bitsy and threw a glance at Itsy while she slept. Tired alright, but at least while asleep, she resembled that girl on terrace who wanted to be best friends with me the other night.

As I boarded an empty 615, I spared a thought about all those itsy, bitsy, tiny, minis who remain under veils back home, only to unveil the rebel in them in an anonymous city like Delhi making full use or misuse of their limited freedom while it lasts.

8

Rag's Crushes

There are two issues which deserve to be treated as topics of PhD thesis rather than being written off in a chapter. They are Shubhra's brain and Rag's crushes. The first issue I am not yet qualified to deal with, hence excluding it from this book. The second one is rather interesting, in which I am still trying to disentangle the webs of mystery.

Approximately on the fourth day of our meeting Rag confided in me while reapplying lipstick in front of CSODR bathroom mirror "I think I like someone." I stopped brushing my hair as I was taken aback:

a. One had not had any meaningful conversation with any guy (except Adhbhut whom Rag did not take seriously)

b. Was I already close enough a friend to share an unfounded love with. May be this is how people get closer.

"Who is the lucky one?" I resumed my combing.

"I don't know him yet. I mean I have seen him a few times hanging around our canteen."

"But all that time you were with me....."

"Yeah, I was. So what? Oh how I wish he notices me."

"OK you must show him to me sometime."

After that she would often tell me nervous, anxious at various sites "Kaya, he is coming, this way, oh my God right here, but don't turn back. Just don't turn back otherwise he will figure out. Oh God, what'll he think about us, those cheap girls, hitting on me."

Then she would whisper "OK now he is right here, don't change your expression, all right?" Some other times she would just point at a crowd of guys and then start "There, there, the tall one in the red t-shirt, the best looking of them all."

But most of the times my myopia got the better of me. Under the spell of my inferiority complex, I didn't choose to wear specs and contact lenses were too much of hassle. So I ended up rubbing my eyes and staring at "the object of desire".

On one hand that embarrassed my friends. On the other, it had the potential danger of sending wrong signals to the guy that instead of Rag, the other girl (I) seemed more interested in him.

Rag and I had been stalking the guy for quite some time now. She had found out his name-Sameer Singvi from Centre for Historical Studies.

In 101, Tapti, I suggested the code name SS, which Rag didn't quite approve "That is the most worn out way yaar, everybody'll find out. Let's call him Red T, most of the times he wears a red t-shirt no!"

Red T was proving to be an elusive darling, always on the move.

One November morning, Rag pressed me, after the class "Kaya let's go for the Presidential debate no."(Election season in JNU)

I found it strange. She was not the political type. She would have sounded more like herself if she had suggested "Let's go to Fab" or "Let's go to Delhi Haat" (remember her obsessive compulsive disorder? The shopaholic thing?)

This is precisely the reason why I looked back at her with disbelief. But she continued unperturbed "Why are you surprised? After all we are in JNU and we should be aware of the political climate here."

I was pleasantly surprised "Of course why not."

Both of us set about walking towards SSS-II (School of Social Sciences) building where the debate was scheduled to be held. Because of heavy unexpected downpour scheduled venue had been shifted from Jhelum Lawns, the historic site of Presidential debate.

As we peeped into the hall, it was jam packed, a crowd bigger than what a Bollywood blockbuster could pull.

I looked at Rag "Are you sure you wanna be ground in this mixer?"

"Now that we have come, let's see for ourselves what this crowd is all about." Just then spotting a bench in the first row getting empty. I quickly rushed towards it "Rag hurry up."

"No Kaya, not in the front, what if they asked you to come to the stage and speak on some burning issues of the campus, worse still the nation, and even worse the world? Let's go to the back."

By that time somebody had already occupied the place I was eyeing. She caught hold of my hand, pulled me with her through the crowd to the second last row.

Though the Presidential debate had a lukewarm opening, somewhere midway it caught fire and I was drawn into it. The mud slinging had just begun when Rag's urgent voice shook me out of my attentive mood "Kaya let's go. Enough of all this." I didn't want to leave "Come on *yaar*! They are just reaching the climax."

"Kaya! Please hurry up. Red T is walking out of the hall."

Unwilling and irritated, I moved out "Oh God! I must have

sacrificed so many afternoons and evenings for a guy with whom I had nothing to do." Madam Rag had acted out the entire farce of becoming suddenly politically aware because of that Red T.

I decided "Enough is enough. I must help Rag talk to Red T. She is not getting anywhere with her love story." And as if God is in the habit of listening to your smaller prayers with more attention than bigger ones, the very next day on my daily trip to home on '615' this guy next to me struck a conversation.

"Are you from CSODR?"

"Yeah, why?"

"No generally, what's your name?"

"Kaya. And you?"

"Sameer Singhvi, CHS."

My senses were awakened instantly "Ohhhhh….!"

Trying to hide my excitement, I hastily added "Heard about you from someone."

We got talking and we actually got along well but my aim was to get Red T and Rag to talk. So I wove a plan in my mind.

"What sort of books do you read?" I treaded on the plan cautiously.

"Well, generally nonfiction."

"What's the latest that you have laid your hands on?"

"Well, I recently bought Amartya Sen's India, Development and Democracy."

"Oh! What a coincidence. I needed to consult that book for my term paper. Looks like God had a purpose in introducing you to me. Can I borrow …."

He cut me in the middle "Why not? You are most welcome.

See, I live in Tapti 245. Why don't you come tomorrow and pick up the book?"

"Thanks a ton. I shall be there."

My plan had hit bull's eye. Next day, I thought I was about to give Rag her greatest surprise and almost expected her to kiss me back in elation. So, at the predetermined time the next day, I called on Red T "Hi! Kaya here. Can you come down and wait in the Tapti lobby? That way, I could pick the book from you."

"Suits me fine."

"OK then. See you in ten minutes."

I rushed to Tapti 101 and broke the news to Rag "Surprise, surprise. Something great is waiting for you downstairs. Come along."

Rag threw a puzzled expression but gave in. In the lobby, Red T was waiting with the black book in his hands. I thanked him and matter of factly introduced "Oh! By the way. She's Rag, my friend. And Rag, this is Sameer from CHS."

Red T smiled pleasantly at her, waving a *hi*, while Rag looked highly uncomfortable wearing one of her rare swollen potato look. She threw a hasty *hi* and turned to me "Kaya, I'm expecting a visitor in my room. I'll see you upstairs."

I somehow knew that not everything had gone right.

While Red T informed me "You can keep the book for as long as you want, I am not really using it now. Do you want to join me for a coffee?" ...

I was more worried and confused about Rag's reaction and actually felt like returning the book to him then and there. But I knew more courtesy than that "No, thanks. Some other time. I shall return this in a day."

"Don't bother." He left.

I rushed upstairs to check the temperature at 101. The swollen potato had grilled further to a swollen tomato. Rag's face was all red. And she appeared as if she would burst into tears any moment now.

That was our first big fight.

She screamed as soon as she caught sight of me "What do you think? You are very smart? Would you care to explain what exactly are you doing?"

"But, I thought…"

"Who the hell allowed you to think on my behalf?"

"But Rag …."

"See all of us have our own lives and just because you are my friend, you can't interfere to any extent, OK?"

"But didn't you…"

"You better don't talk to me. Looks like the way we function is very different. And what you did was horrible."

"OK. Enough." I raised my voice "I thought you liked the guy and will appreciate this."

"To hell with you."

"Same to you."

Shubhra sat quietly on the heap of old newspaper used as a settee in 101 resting her hand on her forehead, with her head bowed down and her eyes staring directly at the floor. If a passerby would care to look through the door ajar, interested in the domestic quarrel, I could bet she would have thought that I and Rag were shouting at Shubhra and she was taking it all sitting quietly.

The fight concluded with both of us crying and Shubhra taking turns to console us.

By midnight, the riot had fizzed out. Tempers had dropped.

Rag approached me first "Kaya you know, please don't bug me like this next time. I mean I never wanted to talk to that guy."

I gave in to her soft voice "But Rag I thought you liked him. I was just helping you fix up."

"But I don't ever want to go around with him. He is just eye candy and I simply enjoyed watching him. I did not want anything beyond that, but now all that is over… I mean it's all right but Red T chapter is closed."

I was perplexed at the fact that how somebody could invest so much of herself, get excited by somebody's presence and still not want to do anything with that person. But Rag was Rag, special and unique.

That night the three of us did not sleep. Over coffee, which Rag and I drank in cups of different sizes and colours, and Shubhra in a curry bowl, we laughed our hearts, lungs and levers out over Rag's past boy friends.

Ragini:

"I had my first boy friend when I was in class 9th. I sported boy-cut hair and had huge specs on, which threatened to fall off my nose anytime. My friends were glamorous by my standards. One after the other, they all managed to have boyfriends. Left alone, it became an ego issue for me. So I pounced on the left over. He was a short Sardar boy whose name was Jagpreet Bahadur Singh Kakkar. He was a neighbour and I fell in love with him the day my mom sent me with sweets to their place. As I climbed upstairs I saw two heads of silky hair hanging from the bed.

I said "Aunty Mom has sent *Mithai*." One silky head turned and there was a guy with extremely pretty face with delicate features. I went flat. Just then the other silky head turned, it was a scary one. A full grown uncle with beard and moustache covering most of his face. Suddenly I felt awkward, as if I had intruded into a private moment.

But after that my boycut and his silky hair complemented each other well. We made up for each other's deficiencies.

Once when our love knew no bounds we got engaged in a house under construction in our backyard. He slipped a ring into my finger and vowed "Till we marry Ragini, this is going to protect our love." My love welled up and spilled over the brim of heart.

The ring shone so bright that it lit up my eyes. Once home I called him up "Jag why did you spend so much? Your words were enough to convince me of your love. By the way was this very expensive?" (Wanting desperately to know the price of the ring)

"Not much, just one-one-five-zero."

"What!" Even though I was overjoyed, externally I had to show my concern "Oh Jag, what was the need for all this? Why did you have to spend eleven hundred fifty?"

"Wait, wait. Just put a dot after one-one."

"You mean eleven rupees fifty paise?"

"Hmmmm"

"OK"

The very next week we broke up over how Jag's flat was too small to accommodate me as Kakkar family *bahu*. I insisted on shifting to another house after marriage and Jag strongly felt that we should stay on with his parents. All of that was in class 10th.

After I came to Delhi, in my first year of graduation, I met Zaheer Abbas. He was from Saudi Arabia, stinking rich. He showered me with gifts every week and I never used to mind. Once he gifted me a goldfish in a fish bowl. I called her Champa Bai, CB fondly. We made promises keeping CB as our witness. Only death can do us part. ... But you know these fish are a lot of trouble.

In the vacations, he went to Abu Dhabi and I packed my bags for Shillong, locking the flat.

After a month when I returned, CB had died a starvation death. I picked up the fish by its tail and put the slimy creature into an empty cigarette box. The next morning, when one of my flat mates put her hand into the cigarette case for her early morning fag, she screamed. The other flat mate of mine was more sensitive than both of us. She suggested that CB was a gift from Zaheer and therefore, she should be buried to attain *Jannat* (heaven).

So the cigarette box acted as the coffin and we buried her in the garden right under our balcony. After making a mound of soil, as we returned to the balcony, we spotted a dog digging into CB's fresh burial spot with its tongue hanging out, saliva drooling. Too lazy to go down again, we ignored him. As Zaheer found out about the treatment meted out to CB, he lost interest in me.

The next two years of my graduation, I was with Pritam Anand, the sports-quota-six-footer and I the five footer.....we got along quite well. He was a soccer player and we gelled well as he let me be. With him I realized that opposites not only attract but also complement. He always brought cartons of golden apple from Himachal, where he had his orchards and considered me to be a thorough intellectual, he himself being from the sports quota. That gave me a new high. I, on my part, would fake coochie cooing kids to impress upon him my sensitive nature.

Once as we sat in a restaurant, I could not suppress a fart loud enough not to be missed by Anand. But he looked the other way as if nothing happened. I said "Don't pretend that you didn't hear."

He indeed was pretending "Hear what?"

"I know that you heard me farting. It's OK Anand it's just human to fart." I said and felt as if it was him who had done the act and I was helping him overcome the embarrassment. But that incident brought us many steps closer in love.

Rag had finished her account.

"But then how did you two break up?"

"Well we never broke up officially but once I came to JNU and he went back to Shimla, the cartons became less frequent. I somehow knew that it was the beginning of the end. As they finally stopped coming, I assumed that the affair had ended."

That night she had very simply through her life experiences made me understand that she was her own person and general rules of life should not be applied and tried upon her. Conversations like these I feel can only take place at nights. There is something about nights when no eye meets the other and communicates 'judgmental responses'. It makes it easier for us to pour our hearts out. As they say, we might hide what we want to by controlling our words, but our eyes say it all. When the darkness of night clouds over those eyes, an open heart surgery becomes relatively easy.

From that day onwards, Shubhra and I fell in love with Rag's love and all of us played the game with utmost seriousness and fun simultaneously. The crowd of crushes that Rag's love files in JNU constitute of...

Code Name	Brief Profile
Gap	Rag found the wide gap between his two frontal teeth very cute.
GG	According to Rag, the perfect looker. Greek God, with a shady girlfriend. He was only two batches junior to us, in the French Graduation classes.
The FFB	The guy always came First For Breakfast and he wore shorts which could qualify as hot pants exposing (in most likelihood intentionally) sexy legs like those of Naomi Campbell.
The Chola King	The South Indian guy Rag had first seen eating *chhole* in the mess. He had long, wavy hair, like that of a king. And Rag felt a current of familiarity with him. May be she had met him in a previous birth when he was the Chola King and she, his queen. Only much later she discovered that her current of familiarity was not unfounded. She had indeed met him before and in this birth only. He played in Rag's ex-boyfriend Anand's soccer team. He had delivered Anand's love letters to her a few times but used to wear his hair short and was tad bit leaner then.

The characters above were just the lead roles in Rag's daily soaps. The second fiddles, sidekicks and other characters if discussed would run into a Ph.D thesis as I had warned you in the beginning.

Nonetheless, the most interesting fact remains that while she shared months of relationship with the lead heroes, she never ever spoke to any of them, did not know the names of most of them and I am not even sure if she remembers all of them today...

As this book took shape, Rag had diligently added many more in the list.

9

Roly-Poly

'Why do we prematurely assume that a girl who is short, stocky, wears her hair like boys, puts on large spectacles with thick glasses cannot have desires of a woman who is beautiful and glamorous?' I asked this question to myself after meeting Roly-Poly in my class.

Roly was Ms chaotic-clumsy-confused. It did not take her more than a few days to declare half the class as her brothers but she couldn't hide her huge crush on talcum white Taran Sharma despite her efforts. Roly's heart raced faster than a racing car whenever Talcum passed by. In other moments when he sat next to her in the class, her racing heart seemed to stop beating altogether. Once our first assignment was allotted, Roly got into the act.

That sultry afternoon, Talcum was busy finishing his assignment in the lab when Roly entered the scene. She spotted an inviting opportune moment. As Talcum drew the boundaries of the Uttar Pradesh map, he heard a voice from behind. Upon turning, he found Roly, who mumbled-jumbled-fumbled without caring to pause at punctuations. That moment she felt weirdly conscious to be left alone with him in a deserted room, imagining the prospect of things that could happen in such a setting. Whoops, just too much.

In her express pace, she rushed "Oh no! You've already spoilt your assignment. Let me do it for you. Once you learn it, you can do it for yourself. Do you have an extra tracing sheet with you or shall I get one?"

Talcum finally got a chance to speak "Yes *yaar* I have three more extra sheets. Take this one *yaar*." And he handed her the sheet.

Roly's hand brushed against his while tracing sheets exchanged hands, she felt butterflies tickling her stomach – the way she generally felt before an interview or just before the question paper was handed out during exams – but something inside told her that she would pass this test, she had enormous confidence in her cartographic skills, if not seducting prowess.

As she started drawing lines of the map, Talcum's eyes grew greedy. Not for Roly, but for the map. She had a perfect hand for drawing. For that assignment both Roly and Talcum earned very good grades.

With a great grade by his side, Talcum thought to himself 'If the price of such great assignments is putting up with this girl, then what's the harm *yaar*?' After that day, Roly and Talcum became cosy twosome.

Roly was a hyperactive kid (so she looked). She managed with a sleep of 3-4 hours everyday. And she loved boys. Boys were her hobby and she dedicated most of her day to that hobby of hers. Talcum remained the first among equals.

Every morning, after getting ready quickly Roly would head straight for Talcum's room. She would wake him up and coax him to hurry up for the class. She cherished this part of the day privately as she secretly imagined herself enacting the role of Talcum's wife. She played a small hubby-wifey game in her mind and lived every moment of the mindgame to the fullest. While Talcum was hardly conscious of Roly's presence in the room (he barely considered Roly a girl), his roomy would signal his discomfort by a few unnecessary unexplained "ch…ch…ch." When that did not change things, he applied for a change of room.

Every night Roly would take an extra class in the Sutlej hostel mess where she would guide all the boys in the class on how to go about their assignments. In special cases, she volunteered to do their assignment herself. But if in her class, she accidentally spotted a girl, her expression grew strangely stern that conveyed very clearly to the discerning intruder 'Get away from here or else…'

She put all her energies into cultivating her hobby. She wanted all the boys at any cost, but Talcum got the best deal of all. He got a home delivery of all necessary stuff at his doorstep, except may be his undergarments. Roly would rush to buy sweets from the market when Talcum's sweet tooth felt an urge. From assignments to tickets, from eggs to laundered clothes, Roly would take care of all of Talcum's needs. In return, she just wanted his warmth and proximity. Given a choice I would have also stepped into Talcum's shoes but did not have the requisite gender qualification to do so.

Talcum was no doubt intellectually one of the dumbest people I had met, but I guess the emotionally dumb part he just chose to act out for his own convenience. He pretended that spending twenty hours a day with a girl did not necessarily mean having to do anything special with her. Theirs was a marriage of convenience.

After a few months of inseparable life, one night Talcum's next roomie showed his annoyance on her presence 24/7. That very day his application for a room change was rejected. Disgusted and bugged to forcibly live in with a girl, he sat on the study chair and made use of body language and para language to indicate what he hesitated to communicate through words owing to his fresh status in the room. What followed was a demonstration of roomie's acting prowess, he made a variety of faces. Roly highly awkward at his reactions saw in it a golden chance to be alone with Talcum, so she suggested "Hey Taran, let's go to the Parthasarathy Rocks. My friends tell me it looks beautiful in these autumn nights."

Talcum had to oblige on these small demands to get the big works done. "Ok let's go. But we must come back early yaar."

"Fine, we'll just have a look at the view and rush back." She was getting too excited just at the prospect of being alone in the dark with Talcum.

As they were reaching the fringes of PSR, a torch light beamed bright on their faces amidst pitch darkness. A legitimate couple (those who are officially going around) among our seniors had spotted both of them in one of the forbidden zones, where you could visit at nights only if you were a couple. And if you were not, you would definitely be pronounced as one.

Talcum got annoyed for he never wanted to be paired romantically with Roly. On the contrary, Roly blushed in the dark as she guessed the consequences rightly. She smiled at the thought of being teased to death the next morning.

Oblivious of Talcum's annoyance in dark, she kept walking estimating the distance between them, she would occasionally try and brush her shoulders against his, making it look like accident blurting an immediate "sorry". His annoyance and her elation knew no bounds. As they reached the spot, a storm engulfed them creating a wild hallucination of intimacy around, the dizzy wind, the veil of darkness drove Roly crazy and she could not resist a strong urge to feel Talcum. In her heights of desire and misty air, she hugged him tight. And he spontaneously flinched responding in a stern tone fuming with rage "What's wrong with you?"

Roly felt as if she had been pushed from the seventh floor. She let go of him in one instant and could not conjure up a better excuse "Oh I thought...I thought it was a tree." Talcum's annoyance turned into anger and his voice had clear sarcasm in it "Oh really. Now that we have seen PSR in an autumn night, can we go back?"

As they headed back towards the habited world, Talcum, the dumb that he was, could not see the tears that were rolling down Roly's cheeks in the dark.

After she had seen him off in his hostel like she did every night, she ran back panting, trying to catch a breath between sobs to find a lonely corner so that she could weep her heart out. She could not find one in the bustling hostel. So she went back to her room where her roomie probed her tight "Why are you crying, tell me?"

Too ashamed to speak the truth, she lied "Nothing, girls in my class are very mean to me because I get along better with boys than any of them." And her sobs grew louder. Not that her room mate believed her but the moment seemed too delicate for a jibe, so she handed her a glass of water and coaxed her to sleep.

As Roly woke up, her eyes all swollen from crying, she felt a ray of optimism within her. She thought it was a new morning. She inwardly wished that all was same with Talcum and he had forgotten everything about the previous night. Even if he had not, she hoped he would overlook it for the sake of the days they had spent together.

She hurriedly dressed up and rushed towards Talcum's hostel. After a moment of hesitation, she knocked. No response from the room. She knocked again.

After a few seconds, his roomie's irritated voice resounded "Taran has left for the Centre."

Roly checked the time. She was not late. She sensed and feared that things would not be same anymore. And she was right. Talcum ignored her royally. Her heart burnt when she saw Talcum sharing a hearty laugh with other girls in the class. When he passed by her and went ahead to sit with someone else, she felt a glass shard pierced her through inflicting her with an unbearable tension in veins.

While her heart was falling apart, the world predictably started teasing her with Talcum. Only after a few days did she realize that she couldn't bear this distance with Talcum anymore. Her love torn heart made a plan.

On that pious day, she knocked Talcum's door again. He opened the door to her, in a cold gesture, he returned to his study table.

Roly followed him and plunged herself on the bed by his side. She banged her hand on his study table when he refused to acknowledge her even after a few minutes passed "Why are you doing this to me Taran? I have always considered you as my brother. I am the only child of my parents and always wanted a brother for myself. When I saw you I instantly knew that you would fill that vaccum in my life. See, see for yourself what I have brought for you, this *rakhi*. Its a bloody *rakhi*, alright?" She was weeping badly by the end of it. May be a tiny hope that lingered on buried deep in her heart was breaking down.

Talcum felt terribly guilty. He extended his hand "Come on. Tie the *rakhi*, now."

Roly tied it with heavy heart and trembling hand, poured water for herself and gulped it down.

One month down the line, Roly recovered and her direction of interest took a 180 degree turn. Her frequency of visit had dwindled from Sutlej-144 and shot up remarkably to room number 212 of Tapti.

Tapti 212 was abode to three guys – two official occupants and the third, a pile on. Of them Neeraj, the Jolly fatso was from Centre for Political Studies. Sriram, the studious boy with a very high probability of cracking the Civil Services was the second official occupant. With the class realizing Talcum's low IQ levels by now, Sriram was on his way to becoming the darling of Maa Go club members. The third illegal occupant was Rajesh Kumar, the Bhojpuri hero with a stumped face, which looked flat as if somebody had just run a steam iron on it, and hairstyle like Shahrukh Khan.

Roly's entry to 212 Tapti meant exit of other girls from that room. She made life hell for those who chose to come even close to the room. She would never acknowledge their presence for one thing. The girls felt as if they were ghosts – invisible and inaudible. The boys noticed all this, but they didn't dare annoy Roly, who took care of all their assignments sparing them a lot of headache and time. They used this time for different purposes. The studious boy crammed for UPSC and Bhojpuri hero flirted with other girls (but outside the room).

Roly forbade the girls in the Centre from approaching the room. "Actually Sriram is studying very hard. He does not like being disturbed at all. So he does not invite many visitors. I have to spend so much time there because I have to do all his assignments so that he can study." Unable to hide her intentions for long, very soon she declared two of the three boys as her brothers – Jolly fatso and Bhojpuri hero. Giving food for thought to all of us

a.   Why did she leave the studious boy?

b.   Why would she take so much care of her brothers' friend?

Talcum had lost his much envied position to the studious boy. Jolly and Roly actually looked like siblings and behaved that way too, with their pillow fights and all that. That evening Roly hushed the Bhojpuri hero and Jolly out of the room and whispered into their ears "I want to talk something really serious with you. How do you think Sriram would react if I tell him that I like him? After all you are my brothers and you must help me out."

Jolly chuckled "*Yaar*, I am very poor in all this. I have never had a girlfriend and I stay away from all this trouble of love, girls, etc. My philosophy in life is to eat cherry, drink sherry and make merry. So I really can't help in all these matters."

Roly turned expectantly to Bhojpuri hero who frowned "See, I always propose to a girl I like only if I see a chance of her saying yes. Sometimes you have to approach indirectly, test the waters, if she sends positive signals, then only you go ahead, otherwise you retreat and try elsewhere. Why to waste time? But I think it is better that instead of us acting as mediators, you tell him yourself." His attitude smacked of people who are more interested in watching the *Tamasha* rather than participating in it.

Roly thought to herself biting her nail 'It is better to try and repent than not try and repent.' So picking up scattered strands of strength, she asked the Bhojpuri hero to send Sriram out. Bhojpuri hero re-entered 212 friskily and hushed in a fishy tone "Boss, you are being summoned outside for something special, Roly is waiting for you. Good luck." And he winked.

Sriram raised his eyes from his books. He wasn't that naïve after all. He had sensed it coming from that very day when he was excluded inexplicably from her band of brotherhood. He had a vague idea that there was more to her feelings than what appeared. Sometimes, he had accidentally side glanced to find Roly secretly admiring him. He had also not missed how possessive she had become of him lately, interrupting him every time he spoke to another girl. He was expecting this but not so soon.

A little uncertain, a little nervous he slid the chair away from the table and moved out. As both of them faced each other, there was an awkward silence, the type that generally precedes a proposing ceremony. Roly broke the ice "As Rajesh would have informed you by now, I want to talk something serious with you. Can we go down and sit on the hostel entrance stairs?"

Sriram was thinking fast of the course of events that were to follow.

"OK let's go." And he thought to himself 'Let her choose the place where she wants to hear this.'

As they settled on the stairs of Tapti, Roly rolled on "OK Sriram, I don't mean to take much of your time. I dont intend to disturb your preparation. How would you react if Rag or Kaya were to propose to you? Would you beat them up?"

Sriram replied trying to appear as calm as he could "No, why should I beat them up?"

Roly lowered her gaze to the floor and muttered faster this time. She could almost hear the sound of her heart beating inside "OK now I am going to tell you something but you promise that you are not going to beat me up for that."

He took a deep breath "Go on."

She continued "Can we be together?"

Meanwhile he was already thinking of a way to convey a "no" that hurts the least "But for that, both the people need to love each other and honestly love is not my priority now."

She could not stop herself and screamed aloud "I knew it, I knew it. Why can't you love me? Why the hell can't you love me? Why can't any guy love me?"

Sriram felt sorry for her immediately but he knew that with his decent looks he could fetch himself a better match. And obviously he could not tell Roly the other truth that his love interest lay elsewhere. So he tried to sound as considerate as was possible "You will also find someone, who is better than me. So don't cry." But Roly's emotional outburst had crossed the Rubicon.

"I don't want anybody better. I want you, you and only you." Her scream-pitch scaling heights every second. Sriram slowly looked up and spotted a few faces enjoying the *tamasha* from the terrace. In the darkness, he could recognize only Bhojpuri hero's and Jolly fatso's face amongst the lot. To save further embarrassment he stood up "Come Roly, I shall drop you back to your hostel." And started walking away from the stairs.

Roly had no choice but to follow him. But she was adamant "You first tell me why you don't love me. I will change myself according to your wishes." Sriram tried to act fatherly "Ok then you first concentrate on your studies fully. Forget love for the time being, get good grades and make your parents proud."

They reached her hostel and Roly stood right beneath the neon street light, illuminated. During the entire conversation, they stood face to face for the first time. He looked at her face, a colour palette where transluscent colour of tears had merged with her nose fluid and it looked like a face of a small fat baby boy who had been denied his favorite toy.

To bid good night, he repeated "Now go back and study hard." He put his hand on her head where her thick wiry hair strands pricked his hand. Before the unassuming needles could pierce him for a blood-test he quickly removed his hand, after patting her head twice, he could feel and smell the oil that her greasy head left on his palms. This gesture of his emboldened her "Ok, you wait. I will study so hard that you will love me one day. I promise you."

She ran back to her hostel as Sriram looked on feeling sorry for her. Back inside the hostel, Roly washed her face in the basin. Looking at her reflection in the mirror, she resolved "I shall make him indebted by doing all his work and he shall have to love me back."

That was the day. After that she completely took charge of all of Sriram's assignments and term papers. Meanwhile, Bhojpuri hero shifted out of 212 Tapti as he was allotted a room of his own. Jolly often felt sorry for Roly when he watched her slogging day-in day-out for Sriram and him not reciprocating.

Roly could sense Jolly's growing sympathy and imposed another relationship on him, her *rakhi* brother Jolly. She made him her agony uncle. It served two purposes—she finally found a friend and that way she could also manage to spend much of her time near Sriram. Often after Sriram slept off, Jolly and Roly would chat away nights altogether. Sometimes in the wee hours when Sriram's sleep broke after a nightmare, he could hear faint whispers in the room. That was when he realized about the strengthening bond between the brother and sister.

During one of those whispering nights Roly got carried away. She whispered in between sobs into Jolly's ears "Imagine my fate. The guy whom I considered my brother fell for me."

Jolly whispered back "What, you mean whom?"

"Taran, who else. One night, as both of us were strolling near

PSR he abruptly hugged me….. Imagine my plight. After all I considered him my brother. So I got startled, asked him for an explanation. It was then that he confided that he liked me in a different way."

"Really!"

"Or why do you think I stopped roaming around with him suddenly? And look at this guy. What all did I not do for him…but he never ever cared."

"I know that part. I have seen it with my own eyes."

Suddenly Roly realized that in the darkness of the room both of them were holding hands and it kind of ….felt good. She waited quietly for a few minutes and then leaned closer. Jolly responded and took Roly in his arms. She felt as if she was melting in the warmth of his embrace. But wait….this did not feel brotherly. On second thoughts, to hell with all that. God knows how many hours passed when Jolly and Roly lay in each others arms – just like that.

The next morning the news spread like fire that a group of four were on a trip to Laddakh. Of the four, two were known to be a couple and the other two, on their way to becoming one – Roly and Jolly. We never quite got to know what happened in Laddakh but what we saw next was Jolly and Roly returned with rosy cheeks and high spirits. It was almost as if Roly carried a loudspeaker screaming into every passerby's ear about how the two had finally found true love.

Now where does that leave Sriram? Sriram was busy studying as usual. Just that he would have to do his own assignments now. In fact the new couple did visit Sriram where Roly broke the news in a very shy tone "That thing has happened between Jolly and me." Sriram finally got rid of some of his guilt.

While speculations were rife with how this relationship was just born out of Jolly's pity and how long it would last, Roly was oblivious to all this. She replaced all off-whites and grays in her wardrobe with pinks and reds. She was too busy walking-sweeping the JNU streets with oversized skirts to be bothered.

Don't get entangled in the maze of how Roly's lover turned her brother and her brother turned into her lover. Think why it happened. This is because there is still a significant part of "modern" society which does not approve of any other close relationship between men and women. It is the compulsion of labelling the relationship of such kinds that gives birth to such dilemmas. A platonic friend must be treated with calculated detachment.

Till this vacuum between lover and brother is given some breathing space, many Roly Polies would fall in and out of such complexities – pasting a name to such relationship and putting them into either-or categories.

10

The Long Village Trip Cut Short

Why does this happen? In every class, love happens in bulk. Not one, two, three, but half of the class falls in love at the same time...sometimes with the same person. Is there a season of love? Does love really have a germination, flowering, maturing, ripening cycle like a fruit or flower? And why do the trips, excursions, study tours form the fertile ground for love to bloom? Ok, too many of them now, the research questions. If a survey can answer so many profound questions, then one does not really expect more out of it.

Shubhra and I posed our chins resting on palms as spectators as Rag popped in and out of three pairs of jeans within a minute. Looks like today is one of her fat days (those days when she realizes that she has put on weight since the day before). And Oh my God! Quick she definitely is. She would change thrice while I still remain undecided about what to wear. As she finally settled into the salwar kurta (which she uses as her weight concealer), Shubhra and I took a deep breath together and glanced at each other which meant 'this is the end of today's fashion show'.

We took the Centre stairs, clambering up two at a time. For the nth time, the Centre's lift was out of order. The third floor

Hall – the door remains one of the solid reasons as to why most of the people make it on time for a class that is to be held on the third floor hall. The door there creaks more than the sound effect used in any ghost serial on TV. That meant a total pause in the lecture, ninety per cent of the class turning their upper halves back to have a look at the culprit and Bichi Roy's withering gaze which meant "you disturbing element".

Today as Bichi lectured us on the topic of our forthcoming survey, "floriculture" for the oncoming village trip, Rag pushed the door. She should have let Shubhra do the job. The door screeched,....khrrrr.... she slipped in and the door screeched back....keeeeen... to its place. It shut right on my face, my nose just saved by an inch or so. One second silence .....two second silence "Shall we ....shall we not?"

The class had resumed after the pause. Opening the door now would be criminal, like taking the blame for two successive screeching sounds. I couldn't have done it alone for life, had Shubhra not been there. Her presence if not legitimized at least diluted the biggest of crimes by her inherent goodness. The door creaked at my slight push. Worse still, I should have pushed it confidently so that one screech and we should have got in.

Instead it jammed midway. Bichi Roy's lecture stopped and her bloodshot gaze was sharp enough to make me feel unwanted (euphemism for what I actually felt). The entire class had once again turned their backs to look at the bold warriors. Time froze. Only the bold warriors hurriedly rushed toward the last bench and sat next to Rag. As Bichi started again, I transferred the same bloodshot gaze, gnawed to my right side where Rag was seated. She cowered her eyes and nodded sideways as if saying "So Sorry". I softened.

The floriculture discussion was in full flow between Bichi Roy and Maa Gos filling up the first two row of benches when she introduced the excursion plan. A part of the plan was even chalked out in Bengali, so we realized that the voice must have come straight from the heart.

After the rough details of the plan were finalized, we were instructed to head towards the supply store and collect the requisite stuff which gave us a feel of an excursion. This remote village "Rangdhuan" in Haryana was supposedly a source area of flowers that made their way to Delhi's wholesale and retail market, from there to the multi-star hotels and rich men's mansions.

As the supply storekeeper counted and threw towards us rucksacks, mats, sleeping bags one after another, we ran to pick up the best ones like ragpickers.

The size of rucksacks measured almost half my height and three-fourth of Rag's. As for Maa Gos, some of them could afford to jump inside the rucksack and zip themselves up along with their stuff. Bichi divided us into different committees – the Transport Committee, Mess Committee and Academic Committee.

1. Transport Committee: Work profile included loading and unloading stuff from the bus, only they were not called coolies.

2. Mess Committee: Who cooked less and did exactly what their name asked them to – "create mess".

3. Academic Committee: Nothing academic about it. They were to keep a check on the stationery, questionnaire and distribute them judiciously.

4. Discipline Committee: Work profile was to make people behave well, a task just next to impossible. Therefore, this was committee "do nothing". Rag and I volunteered to be part of this one, citing our leadership skills in schools. We dragged Shubhra into it as well.

That night I stuffed in all the unused cosmetics my relatives had fetched us from abroad as if I was on my way to participate in a beauty contest. For 21 days I must have packed moisturizers of three different brands, a perfume, a deo, 6-7 shades of lipstick, cleanser, toner, body shower gel of three different types. Just then my mom screamed from the kitchen.

"Packed up your stuff?"

"Yeah Ma. Almost."

"Where did you keep your toothbrush and paste? In the side pockets?"

"Totally forgot about them."

"I knew it ..... Without me not a single thing would function right in this house."

"What would happen to me without my good old Ma!"

Early in the morning I had to coax my sister to drive me to JNU. She grumbled but finally gave in with a grumpy face. I made it to Tapti hostel on time, the venue from where we were to leave for the village.

As the minibus, with CSODR pasted all over, halted with a screech before us we saw the transport committee convenor, Bhojpuri Hero, climbing up the CSODR minibus and standing in his typical way, ruffling his Shahrukh Khan hair with his right hand.

And so the roof of the minibus grew several feet taller with our rucksacks together looking like a bunch of army men in uniform. Once the stuff got packed, it was time to pack ourselves into the minibus. One after another, 35 of us cosied into the minibus originally meant for 20. On a chilly December morning in Delhi, you couldn't have asked for a better heater.

The sitting arrangements broadly resembled the positions

around the bonfire near PSR, and changes in relations, affiliations and coalitions since then.

Two such clear changes were:

i) The anglicized Maa Go, Engli, who had scored very low on the Oomphometer had drifted away from the club to our camp and sat next to me.

ii) Another ex-Maa Go, Tara who originally hailed from U.P. but had spent her life in Kolkata had deserted the club owing to the step sisterly treatment meted out to her by 'pure' Bongs. She left the club for Dard – the Pain. Both coochi-cooed for a while, just when rumours and speculations were ripening into truth on the basis of scattered evidence by dispersed witnesses, Tara had coolly dumped him. She had graduated to a better beau (only relatively).

She sat on the last corner-most seat with her new beau Amar, rather almost on him, cribbing once a while about the lack of space. Nothing missed the eyes of the Maa Go club. The MG club had strong anti-defection rules where defectors like Tara and Engli were treated with greater contempt than us because we were the foreigners, the aliens, and they the defectors, the traitors.

As Tara snuggled besides Amar I could hear from the seat just in front of me, Shampa's voice.

"*Maa go*, look at what this girl is upto. You have to have a little shame. Do what you want to in your hostel room. *Na na cholbena cholbena*…(won't do, won't do)."

Another Maa Go Jhumpa from the seat ahead "*Kee rey*, tell me also." Whispers, giggles, more whispers, more giggles.

The last I could hear was "*Maane* (meaning) there has to be *leemit* to everything."

With those words I dozed off. Must have been an hour later, when I woke up to find the rest of them either asleep or half asleep. Engli's head almost on me, with her mouth open resembling the mouth of a well. The only noise I could hear was that of Rag from one seat behind.

She was bargaining something with Pinaki. Rag's voice "Listen anyway I caught you sleeping alright? So why don't you just hand over the walkman to me. You were wasting battery. I switched it off, otherwise you would have run out of battery. Come on just for 15 minutes."

"But now *toh* I am wide awake and I want to *leessen* to my own walkman. Anyway, after one more *shong*, I have three *fabhourite shongs* coming up in a row."

"Ok, then ask Urboshi to vacate the seat next to you so that I can have one of your earphones, at least."

"Fine, *Ae* Urboshi. Get up *re*. Rag wants to *shit* here for sometime."

I couldn't suppress a laugh. Just then I felt a smack on my head. That was Rag, a good trader always….clinching a profitable deal.

After a few halts, a look here and there at the flower gardens in other villages, a dhaba here, a dhaba there, we reached our destination. Dusk was giving way to darkness. For the night we were to live a few kilometres away from the village. A dilapidated house for the girls, a broken, abandoned school for the boys to serve as our night shelters.

The house owner's voice was sandy; the types where you always want to tell the person to clear his throat first. Putting aside his *hukka*, the burly man bragged brusquely in front of my professor.

"Whatever you say, it is a huge responsibility to let so many girls stay at one's place. No one except a really courageous man (implying himself) would let them in for a night. Just instruct your girls not to wander around too much, it is not safe. Not only in terms of outsider men, but hyenas, wolves that have been spotted in the sugarcane fields right in front."

He hesitatingly added, this time his voice a little low "Also there is a problem of water here. So tell them to use the bathroom and toilet sparingly." (as if it were in somebody's mighty control to use it or not)

Prof. Bhanu asked "Would the boys be OK and safe in that broken school nearby?"

A thunderous laughter echoed and he continued "Boys, if they can't take care of themselves ...deserve to be roughed up anyway."

To that my nonstop chitter-chatter Prof. also fell silent.

After her talk with the house owner, she repeated the same instructions to the girls "Do not unnecessarily loiter here and there. Remember this is not Delhi (as if Delhi was meant to be safer) and keep a control on your nature's calls. The man does not want us to visit his loo too much. For that I will advice an early sleep. I and Madam (Bichitra Roy) will sleep with the lady of the house. For you they have vacated the store room on the terrace. It is just one night, so you can do without fan. It is December anyway, come on follow me now."

She led us to an even more dilapidated room where a broken double bed without a mattress occupied two-third of the space. She continued "Five-six of you can manage on the bed (a bed that was supposed to sustain two people). Actually the iron bed is too heavy to be lifted out of the room. It is a matter of one night after all. Tomorrow morning we head towards Rangdhuan and start our floriculture survey." She had almost gone out of the room when she peeped again.

"And do not bother to check the boy's section, they will be perfectly safe" adding in a fishy tone as if to mean 'in Haryana, you can not trust even these boys.'

Some of the girls laid their sleeping bags quickly on the floor. Remaining six of us tried to adjust on bed with our upper halves (till knees or thigh depending on our heights) resting on the bed, the remaining hanging out of it. Two of Maa Gos even had to sleep on the ground floor of the bed – just under the bed.

When all of us had fitted in the jigsaw fit, Rag's voice rose above the cramped existence "Anybody for loo? Girls, anybody?"

At least three-four 'Yeah, yeah', 'Me too' echoed. A small brigade got up disturbing the equilibrium of the jigsaw puzzle in the room.

They tiptoed their way downstairs not intending to disturb Profs' sleep.

I dozed off again.

After what felt like half an hour, whispers of five odd people woke me up.

a) Whispers of five people could be more disturbing than a loud scream when you are half asleep.

b) If I had escaped the whisper, a push here and an elbow there could not have left me undisturbed.

I do not know exactly which one of the above finally jolted me out of sleep. To my surprise I was not the only one as the readjustment process drew many an irritated "ch….ch" throughout the room. Suddenly I felt the need to visit the loo. As Rag was pushing me to make place for herself on the bed, I whispered into her ears "How was the loo? okayish?"

As if something had triggered her emotion, leaving her efforts to lie down halfway, she sat erect "Okayish? Are you mad or what?

Firstly, I am not sure where I peed was the bathroom or something else."

"What?"

"Yes madam!" She continued "It was pitch dark there downstairs. And whatever looked like a loo did not have a door. It just had a curtain, that too not full length, something like a midi length skirt. As I stepped in, I figured out something vaguely resembling a toilet that had no roof. You feel bare and exposed there. The moment I settled myself to do the business, I heard giggles' which did not come from outside but from the terrace.

When I looked above at the roofless top from where the sound had travelled downstairs, I spotted something in the dark that I had not till now. There were clean staircases which invitingly ran from terrace to the place where I was stuck. I froze. For all you know, someone had caught me in the act and was having a good laugh over it. Imagine.

That's not all. As we rushed upstairs, Prof. Bhanu woke up and screamed behind our back '*inform your friends not to use the loo anymore and control till the morning. You people have to do things which you are told not to*'....as if we had committed some sin."

Knowing the conformist that I was, the loo visit was out of question now and the description of the deadly experience doubly supported the decision I had just arrived at. Somehow I cajoled myself back into sleep with my legs dangling out of the bed. I am not sure whether I was asleep, awake or somewhere between that when Engli's desperate plea ringed in my ears.

"Kaya, can you come with me to the loo? It is urgent."

The smartest thing to do was to pretend to sleep but smartest moves are meant for smart ones "You know, ma'am has just warned Rag and all not to use it again. We might get into trouble."

She graduated up the level of urgency in tone and words.

"We will go to the fields, anywhere…it's an emergency you know Kaya. Otherwise, I would not bother you."

I mean if she were an old friend I would have made her understand that controlling is better than Bichi Roy grading us three grades lower. If she were 'not a friend' I would not have bothered to think of what she would think of me. But she was a new friend and this was the time when it seems most difficult to throw a request out of the window. Therefore, I agreed.

To muster up courage, I stroked Shubhra 'the pillar of legitimacy' and the one man rescue team who has a way out of every problem without fussing much over it. She readily agreed. That is the difference between good souls and ordinary girls, between Shubhra and me.

The three of us ventured out. Using the loo was out of question. "The next best option is the endless sugarcane fields" I suggested.

Engli lost her senses "Are you nuts? What if a snake bites me there? You want the world to know that I died while peeing in a sugarcane field? I deserve a more dignified exit from the world."

"Listen Engli, there is no place else that we know of. This is a goddamn house and the adjacent one is the broken school where the boys are staying. Now you can't possibly go there. If you hazard a thought of getting caught in the act by one of the boys, you probably would prefer a death in sugarcane fields to life after that."

Poor Engli frowned "OK. What difficult decisions to make in life. It is like a choice between eating rotten meat and dying of hunger. I think I prefer the cane fields."

We pawed our way out of the building like cats. How much ever I had convinced Engli, the whole scene looked damn scary and I was already repenting the decision. But now having gotten this far I could not deny her the right to such a basic need.

We had reached the edge of cane fields "Go Engli. Don't think. Just go, do it."

I sounded like a commander sending his soldiers to the battlefield. While I said so, my eyes were closed and I was remembering Lord Hanuman, the Hindu functional God to ward away evil spirit. I could bet that Engli too had her eyes shut remembering her closest and only approximation Lord Jesus.

And Engli disappeared in the cane fields. After what must be a few minutes she emerged back, her face relieved, she herself safe and in sound health.

Just when Shubhra and I heaved a sigh of relief assuming that the rest of the journey is going to be a lot easier, there was a hush-hush in the canefields right behind Engli. Engli reflexively turned back. The hush-hush grew louder. And this was the moment.

I could hear Shubhra mumble under breath, softly, unconvinced "Just a dog or cat Engli. Let's rush back." I managed to suppress a squeal by putting my hand on my mouth. But before we knew any thing else, the world was waking up to a scream. I tried to search whether my throat had ditched my attempt, but no, that was Engli shouting from the rooftop. The first to arrive on the scene was this lanky villager who probably had come to the spot to perform the same task as us.

Engli managed to give a clue "I think I caught glimpse of a man's shadow here."

The villager pounced into the cane field and disappeared.

We came back to our senses. Engli had regained her composure.

"I am sorry for the mess, should have more control on vocal chord. What next?"

I hadn't given up all hopes "May be we can still make it to the room without anyone getting to know that it was us."

"OK let's hurry up."

We started our marathon back. A few meters away from the gate to the house, two gleaming petromax lanterns shone in the dark.

Caught. Our cabal' was exposed.

"No point tricking them anymore Engli."

Bhanu and Bichi's image became clearer as the distance between us shrinked. A little closer and we could even see the CSODR engraved on petromax lanterns. A very unfriendly voice greeted us "What are you up to girls?"

Now we could also spot a few Maa Gos behind, the house owner with a disgusted expression of "you miscreants" and a few of the boys whose expressions I had not analyzed.

We on our part narrated the story unedited, without hiding any details.

Bichi frowned "I think before retreating, we can have a look at the scene." She sounded nothing less than a Crime Bureau Inspector. As we headed back towards the cane field, we saw three heads emerging from darkness, two of them bowed down, one held high. Probably the man who had disappeared into the fields, I thought.

As the images became sharper, the picture too became clearer.

While the man walked like a fisherman with his prized catch, the other two bowed heads were those of Tara and Amar. Suddenly our crime faded into background as the fresh culprits stood in front. After a few moments of silence, Bichi probed "Speak up. What's your defence?"

In an instant she switched jobs, from Crime Bureau Inspector to that of a Judicial body. While Amar stayed quiet, his head still hung low with shame, Tara spinned the yarn "Sorry Ma'am, for the trouble. Actually I had come to attend nature's call and I think Amar had come to do the same. Coincidentally we met ......but just then we heard someone approaching us from behind. Thinking that they might misunderstand us, we tried to hide. And rest..... is known to all."

I thought 'This is called 'Absence of Mind.' The lamest, lousiest of excuse I have heard in years.'

Ma'am apologized to the house owner and excused herself to be with the culprits (or victims of Engli's nature's call – whatever you choose to call them).

We skipped the rest by escaping the scene while we still heard Bichi's voice "Whatever has happened is over. Do not spread the word around."

These words to the Maa Gos? Think twice, ma'am. After all, you must have been one yourself long back.

Next morning we were off to Rangdhuan. As we waved the house owner goodbye, for the first time he looked relieved. The house blurred in our vision, new fields of sugarcane, mustard, marigold and gladioli crossed us one by one. On reaching the village, we headed straight towards *Chowdhary*'s (headman) place.

At his courtyard, we made space for ourselves everywhere, over the charpoy, on the pavement and railing. Tara was busy chatting away to glory with the woman of the house as if nothing had happened yesterday.

Rag whispered into my ears below the mango tree, on the rounded pavement of cement "Looks like Tara has vowed to become *Chowdhrain* (headman's daughter-in-law) today. Do you want to come for a recci (reconnaissance) with Shubhra and me?"

The three of us went around looking at this world so different from ours, so close in distance and yet so far in life. So colourful and beautiful, yet so smelly and stinky.

That was my first encounter with Gaana, the little cute baby who wore a bodice, a flowing skirt with her big belly staring out in-between. Her mother Sinduri was busy wiping grime out of Chowdhary's utensils.

Everything about Gaana was cute except for the running nosy. I have a mental block. I just can't cuddle kids with nosy running. Gaana and her mom took a break from their work and stared at us as things of amusement. The same way as we did at a picturescape which could very well be hanging at any posh villa of Delhi. Two pretty faces, sharp knife-edge features providing strength to those faces, a bronze tan for which a Delhi Page 3 model could spend thousands of bucks, junk jewellery (in which Rag seemed most interested right now) that could cost a fortune in the *Santushti complex* or any upmarket designer store and the piercing gaze, with their shy smiles, priceless and not saleable in any store of Delhi.

As Sinduri stood up, her bloated belly indicated her matured pregnancy. My thought process was broken by Rag's enquiry "Where can one buy these pieces of jewellery? These toe rings, nose rings and bracelet?"

Sinduri answered, excited at the appreciation "The Thursday Haat Bazaar near MewaLal's Kothi."

Shubhra was trying to cuddle Gaana's cheeks but Gaana was shying away, hiding herself in her Mom's bloated belly.

Engli's call reminded us that we had to be back in the courtyard "Hey girls! What are you doing here? We have had two rounds of yummy *lassi* there, we will also have to leave for the place we are to stay in, come on."

As we stood up, Rag and Shubhra grumbled over missing the *lassi* part. We reached the courtyard and I turned back to sit on the pavement, that was when I realized that Gaana had followed us all the way. But the moment I extended my hand asking her to come near, she giggled and ran away.

We reached Mewalal's Kothi where we were to live. Interesting construction. They lived downstairs and vacated the first floor for us, which had a square shaped hole just above the square courtyard so that sunlight could seep through, a common feature of most North Indian rural houses.

For the girls a shack-converted loo was erected three houses away, for boys the loo stood three lanes away. We settled into our modified existence. Coming back to where we started, although life seemed terribly difficult, love was brewing in the class.

a) Tara and Amar who solemnized their love story in the cane fields where Engli peed.

b) Bhojpuri hero who ruffled his hair and broke into a smile every time Mewalal's pretty teenaged daughter burst into scene.

c) Rag, who covered maximum households for the survey so that she could gobble down variety of milk food.

d) Gaana's love for me.

To my surprise, Sinduri and Gaana worked for Mewalal too.

As our Profs prepared us for the floriculture survey, they divided us into groups, handed us questionnaires, of which we were to fill up ten each in a day based on interviews with the farmers. I was paired up with Tara, Rag with Sriram and Shubhra with Pinaki.

On the first day of the survey as we climbed downstairs, I chanced upon Mewalal's teenaged daughter stealing glances coyly upwards. Just reconfirmed. Bhojpuri Hero was standing up there with a triangle between his legs (which the Maa Gos called Gateway of India) pretending to be cleaning his shoes. Suddenly someone grabbed my knees. I lowered my gaze to find Gaana. Today, face-freshly-washed, nosy-leak-fixed, she looked temptingly cute so I planted a peck on her cheek and went out to the fields.

The farmers were busy working. They would not take us seriously.

My first victim – Bholaram.

He queried us on why were we filling those forms. Would we inform the Govt. back in Delhi about their water-electricity problems? Would the Govt. then intervene?

On knowing that none of this was going to happen, he concluded that we were a useless bunch. As he watered the marigold, we went through the questionnaire hurriedly lest he changed his mind. He skipped a few answers.

As we moved on, the next field had kids playing in it. They took us to their houses. On my way, I chanced upon a few friends. I also met Rag and Sriram—Sriram taking notes from an old man and Rag busy with a steel bowl of kheer.

The following day we crossed path with Engli who was quizzing a villager riding a bullock cart full of dried *gobar* (cow dung).

"Bhaiya is this your *Gobar*?"

"No sister it is most definitely my buffalo's" replied the cart rider with a mocking smile.

There was a repeat telecast of some scenes. Sriram busy taking notes while Rag devouring a bowl of *malai* and *gur* waving at me.

As I reached back, I found Gaana eagerly waiting to play with me. I realized I too had started looking forward to meet her.

Village life we realized was about a lot of hardwork and happiness. There were reasons galore to crib about but I felt time ticked very slowly there-relaxed, chilled out giving life a chance to live every passing moment. Rural hardships didn't go easy with urban crowd.

Tara fell ill. In the night when most of us had slid back into our own sleeping bags, a few still debated furiously over the topic of who the big snorers were. The two accused were defiantly refusing the charge when Engli entered the room with a hint of panic on her face.

"Something has happened to Tara. She might be having an epileptic attack."

All of us ran to see, to help and find out. We found Tara convulsing uncontrollably, her body rising and falling as Sriram and Amar struggled with all their might to control her. Only respite was no foam oozed out of her mouth.

Bichi and Bhanu panicked too. They deliberated on the option of calling the ambulance from nearby town, by then Tara had sobered down and managed meekly "Don't bother ma'am. I get such fits once a while."

In the days that followed, we felt the resistance among farmers to reply candidly to our question grow. Probably they didn't want to waste much of their precious time on jeans clad, gum chewing aliens who had no immediate solutions to any of their pressing problems. This trip was our first brush with the reality of research and seriousness of life.

By now we all met each other frequently in the fields, doctoring data and tallying inter-group questionnaires there. This act was meant to impose some form of standardization on how much manure the farmers put, how much artificial fertilizer they used, which season they sowed their seeds, the quantity and price of seeds, etc, etc.

The truth of life had started taking serious toll on my classmates, people were falling sick in dozens. Headaches, running nose, sore throat, loose motion, spinal chord problems, cracked heels rained in wholesale. Even Tara convulsed again on that rainy night. Amar, secretary of Transport Committee along with the Profs had gone to fetch flour for chapatis. So Sriram and Shubhra rushed to her aid. On his return, Amar thanked Sriram many times over for the favour.

The next morning, assuming that Tara was weak and ailing, I advised her against coming with me but she shrugged it off "You can't stop living life for the fear of dying." She philosophised looking into the mirror and smearing a shocking pink lipstick on her lips to match her *kurta* for the survey.

During this period I had made friends with some of the womenfolk of village who secretly fed us with delicious oil-rich lunch, milk desserts and chatted with us. One of them, Lali had become specially close to me. From her I learnt a lot about their lives. She confided that they could not come to meet us more often because they were not allowed to step out of the houses without permission but they could have loads of fun inside their houses. Lali came to my rescue everytime Tara left me in a lurch and fled to meet Amar. But that day even Lali ditched me.

On that morning the fields looked deserted, almost ghostly and there was a studied silence about the village. No one turned up for work. Once again there had been a still born baby. The villagers considered this inauspicious, a curse of Mata Saru, their village deity. That day even Lali pleaded helplessness "My father-in-law, husband are at home today. I hope you understand. I shall meet you later, have to attend to them now." Bereft of roof I had no choice but to relax in the abandoned fields.

Tara predictably excused herself to meet Amar and left. She often did that but all those days I used to have the roof to my rescue. Today, I sat in midst of mustard and marigold, and my mind wandered 'The fields look so picturesque exactly the way they show in Hindi movies – in *Silsila* and *DDLJ*. But when Rekha ran through those gardens with that romantic take-me-in-your-arms expression, did she also inhale the foul smell of compost which is assaulting my nose now?'

Alone in the field, I suddenly missed home like never before. I hid my face in my lap, shed a few tears and drifted between sleep and wakefulness with the sun warming me on that December morning.

By the time I woke up, the sun's cosy warmth had transformed into harsh heat but there were no signs of Tara. Generally she came back in an hour. To check on time my eyes searched for the wristwatch, but probably I had left it back at the *Kothi*.

'But I must look for Tara.' I did not know where to find her. Still I had to start, if I must return alone there would be questions asked and Tara would mind. So I searched the mustard fields, the marigold fields, beyond that the gladioli fields and the pond side. Where had she disappeared? The last corner was the patch of poplar trees, the branch of which lit our homes—used to make matchsticks.

My eyes fell on uniformly spaced poplars once, the beauty of symmetry invited me in. If only I could find Rag or Shubhra or even Engli, I would revisit this place in the second half of the day.

Suppressing my greed, I turned my back to poplar trees and

---

* Dilwale Dulhaniya Le Jayenge.

walked away. On my way back, I chanced upon Engli and Pinaki arguing over something. I extended an invitation to Engli to join me for a walk in the poplar patch in the second half. She jumped "Why can't we do it now? Nobody is there in the fields anyway Do you know how the entire village is mourning the still born baby?"

"But isn't it time already for lunch?"

"No it is just 12.30." She reconfirmed by throwing a glance at her wrist.

"Oh! Actually I lost track of time. Fine let's go now."

Pinaki excused himself and both of us went back to the poplar patch. As we strolled through the manmade woods, sharing our experiences, I suddenly spotted a hint of pink.

From a distance, I could see Tara convulsing uncontrollably and Sriram struggling to contain her. As I rushed to help instinctively in their direction, I felt my hand being pulled from behind. It was Engli tugging at my hand and put her finger on her mouth indicating me to keep quiet.

As I retreated, my steps, she whispered into my ears "Look carefully. What do you think? Is she really ill?"

I too lowered my voice "What do you mean?" Guessing vaguely what she meant.

As I looked on, I could see Tara's hand firmly gripping the back of Sriram and more….

Engli continued "Everybody knows, at least Maa Gos know about it. Why does she convulse only when Sriram happens to be around? Why does she refuse to be taken to the hospital? How does she manage not to feel weak after convulsing thrice in six days? Don't you remember how she dumped *Dard* like hot potato when she found Amar responding to her sighs? Let's just walk back, man."

What Engli was saying was not completely unfounded. And I added my own questions to it. If she had been occasionally convulsing since childhood, as she claimed, why had we not heard about it ever before the trip? Questions popped one after another in my mind and I tried to stop thinking about Tara.

On reaching back, I found Gaana delighted, gradually getting comfortable, opening up to me. She frog-jumped from her mom's lap and tugged at the end of my *kurta* planting a peck on my hand. Sinduri appeared exhausted-weak and her stomach seemed ready to deliver any moment now. I gave her some unsolicited advice "Sinduri it is time you take some rest."

By now it was a known thing that we had bungled up the Floriculture Survey, it had flopped big time. Bichi and Bhanu in a way knew it in their hearts of heart. So, they did not press us anymore to work overtime.

Tonight we were to throw a formal feast for the village people who had supposedly helped us. That was how a research survey was supposed to end in a CSODR trip. So we roamed home to home inviting them for dinner. I extended a special invitation to Lali, who had given me a roof over my head all those afternoons when Tara left me to meet Amar....or someone else...or whosoever.

Habitually, covering her head with *pallu*, Lali sounded apologetic

"I don't think I can, I don't think any young woman will turn up in your feast."

"But why?"

"I already told you we cannot move about in the village freely the way you do. We are the daughters-in-law of the village, the "*izzat*" of village and anyway the villagers are already complaining about some objectionable things that they have lately spotted. My father-in-law thinks you are corrupting the culture of our village and it was unethical on *Chowdhary's* (Headman's) part to let you in for a month."

"But do you wish from your heart to come to our feast or not?"

She fell quiet for a long time. I thought she would not answer but she did "I very much wish to….and so do other girls and daughters-in-law."

"But you can't."

"No we can't."

"OK then. We are leaving in three days. I don't think then we will meet again."

"Give me your address. I'll write letters to you." She instantly ran to fetch a pen and paper.

"Can you read and write?" Pleasantly surprised on her belated enthusiasm I asked simultaneously scribbling on the sheet my address, then cutting the whole thing to rewrite the same in Hindi.

"Yes I have done B.A."

"That's good…Hope we will be touch."

I looked for Sinduri and Gaana to invite but couldn't find them. The feast was as big a disaster as the survey. A few men did turn up, behaved civil but that was about it. At the end the house owner distributed sweets after breaking the good news that her sixteen year old has found a great match in Ludhiana. I instantly looked at the Bhojpuri Hero, he hid behind the pillar.

Sinduri did not turn up for work, second day in a row. But today as I and Shubhra went out for a walk though fields, we spotted Gaana walking aimlessly on the dusty sand track all by herself. I grabbed her by arm only to find her nosy running in full flow. Instead of delightfully squealing she started crying abruptly. In the last twenty days with her, I had never seen her like this. So to calm her down, I tried distracting her.

"So tell me Gaana, did you already have a baby brother or a baby sister?"

Suddenly she stopped crying "Yes my mother produced a baby…"

"Wow you have a live doll now." I comforted her by wiping her overflowing nosy with her own skirt.

"No…..my *daadi* said….the bitch has again borne a bitch."

My heart started sinking.

"And then?" I probed.

"Then the baby heard it and cried and cried. My *daadi* fed her those leaves so that she wouldn't cry anymore……so that she could sleep….without bad dreams….then in the night my *baba* and *daadi* carried the baby away."

"Where?"

"I don't know….must be the mango tree where they bury the witch children."

"Where is Sinduri?"

"She is sleeping since then."

"Have you seen more burials under mango tree?"

"I don't know *didi* … I don't know…. I don't want to talk." She resumed crying.

My heart melted for her. For the first time I realized she had spoken so many words and she might not be as young as I thought her to be.

As I took her in my arms with Shubhra cuddling her back, I let her do something I had never allowed my own niece and nephews to. I let her running nosy soil my clothes as her sobs buried into me.

I picked her up and guided by her direction, took her to her hut, where an old woman squatted on a charpoy.

"*Arey* what? This girl is troubling you or what?" She asked.

I retorted sternly "What news of Sinduri?"

The old woman made a sorry face "Poor woman, she delivered a still born child. She is weak and hurting. I will send her for work tomorrow."

"Can we see her?"

She hesitantly added "OK for a minute. But she is not well…remember."

We quickly entered the hut. There lied Sinduri, weak, hurting and stone faced.

The old woman caught me by hand and led us out. My eyes wandered once for Gaana. She had fallen asleep on the woven charpoy. My heart went out to her; but the old woman had grown suspicious by then.

So, Shubhra and I left.

"Kaya do you realise the still born child could very well be case of female infanticide?"

"Not could, Shubhra, it most definitely is." A shudder ran down my spine.

"What can we do about it?"

"Let's confirm it."

"Where from?"

"Come with me."

We sprinted faster to head straight to Lali, whom I had waved good bye two days back. I knocked.

Her face brightened up to see me. But without returning her enthusiasm, I pounced on the matter "Lali, in your village are their cases where female babies are buried alive?"

Her face lost colour. She nervously fumbled "I don't know what you are talking about. I have no idea."

"Lali don't be scared. I am your friend I will tell no one that you told me."

"This is a village *didi*. Everybody already knows that whatever you know about this village has to be from me. And after you leave, I'll have to suffer."

"OK tell me the other still born child that you had a few days back. Was it a girl child too?"

She bowed her head.

"I can't lie to you *didi*. Yes it was. But please don't ask me anything more. I will be in trouble for this. Please I beg you."

Something told me it was not a great idea to carry on there for long.

Therefore Shubhra and I headed back. As we rushed out, in the courtyard I could feel Lali's husband's disapproving gaze on us.

I discussed the issue with Shubhra and decided we could not just sit back.

We went to Bichi and Bhanu, narrated the entire incident as we witnessed their eyes and mouth widening apart. It was Bichi's idea. She turned to Bhanu "Madam, let us quickly do a sample survey on female infanticide. This floriculture thing anyway did not work out fine."

"But Bichitra, where are the questionnaires? How will we manage without demarcating the sample formally?"

"Chuck all that Madam. Tonight we sit and prepare a semi-structured questionnaire. Leave it open ended so that we can gain maximum information."

Suddenly I heard Shubhra interrupting them and speaking my mind "But ma'am what about Sinduri? What about the issue?"

Bichi stopped and threw a helpless look at us "*Beta* we know this is not even injustice, this is sin. But please understand that we are guests here. Are you ready to stay back and fight for Sinduri for years and bear the consequences? The only way we can make a difference is through a research paper that can reach the Govt."

She could not convince us but we were not the bravest of souls. We surrendered and that whole night we burnt up fuel to prepare questionnaire with indirect questions meant to derive as much information as possible. The class was in mission mode. Just before the break of dawn, one by one we collapsed on floor mats.

My sleep was broken by loud noises from outside. I woke up Shubhra and Rag. As we went out, a few of the boys were already awake and standing outside the room from which the noise emerged.

The headman, Lali's husband and two more men had marched into the house screaming at the Profs.

We could only hear the heated exchange in parts. "We are leaving you unharmed only because you are ladies and our guests. But we are also warning you, you too have many girls whose safety is your responsibility. Leave the village by noon or else don't blame us …. You crossed the line…In the guise of floriculture, you interfere in internal matters. Just leave the village…" They stomped out in fury.

Bichi and Bhanu came out looking weary and tired "Don't ask questions. Pack your bags. We are leaving within two hours."

Pinaki resisted "But Ma'am, what about the questionnaire we prepared the last night, working so hard on it."

"Throw it in the dustbin. And no more questions. Go wake up your friends and tell them to get ready."

As we mounted the bus with heavy hearts, I saw what I dreaded – Gaana and Sinduri. Sinduri looked weird with a flat stomach, I imagined she always had a bloated belly. I went up to them. She forced something into my hand "For you and your friends." I kissed Gaana on cheek and trudged back. As the bus roared with the ignition, I opened my clutch to find three pairs of toe rings, wrapped in a newspaper.

As the bus left the village behind, I looked through the window and thought to myself.

"Someday, when I author my first book, I will write about this village, where women are imprisoned in the cage of love and culture, where mustard and marigold shine beautifully under sun and beneath them lie buried small baby girls who were denied their first right to cry and their first right to live."

11

Roaring Lion to Cuddly Mommy

Do not mistake the title to imply that JNU is a zoo and a comforting home to me at the same time. This is just the second part of the promise I made to you to show the varied range of faculty that JNU offers.

Second semester brought with it a few repetitions, a few more specimen and exactly those many shocks to students. Only the new ones would be taken up for detailed study sparing the rest (who might claim double jeopardy otherwise).

The roaring lion Mahinder Partap Sekhon

We always knew that we would get a warning bell before his grand entry. We had seen him before and were sure that his paunch would definitely enter into the classroom before he himself did (Till the day he decides to walk backwards into the classroom). In that fraction of a second the anarchy of the class would transform into an obedient humble group only wanting to learn, learn and learn more.

The very first day he entered the class, the banter, chitter-chatter, croaking, crooning wore a veil of silence as we put on our acting masks, quite like a railway station turning into a hospital, a fish market into a library. He made himself comfortable and swept the entire class with one glance. His glance abruptly stopped right in the middle of the second bench and he roared. "Can you start introducing yourselves, from right there, in the middle?"

Right there in the middle I found myself stranded. I managed to introduce myself with an artificially induced confidence without messing up my name, the name of the college I had graduated from and my address. As I reclined back on the chair, I could see some admiring glances from my classmates for not having faltered and I myself felt nothing less than winning a small time neighbourhood competition.

But after me it was Rag's turn and she did not share a similar experience. She hurried through her introduction nervously and as she was sitting back, she was summoned yet again by another roar "Hansraj College, hmm. Who is the principal there?"

I am not sure whether it was the unprepared moment or her lack of alertness, but her memory had ditched her at the worst moment. She stood up again, looking at the fan, then at me, then at Adhbhut, expecting us to pass on a clue. Her face resembled that of a baby who had been asked to recite a forgotten rhyme.

Adhbhut tried his best to remind her "It's Bhim….Bhim" he said in a hush-hush tone and Rag took her cue.

Her face lit up like a 200 watt bulb as she uttered "Bhim Sen Joshi."

What followed scared everybody. Mahinder Partap Sekhon burst out laughing uncontrollably, his roaring laughter inspired nervous laughs throughout the class, who laughed with him. I think just to give him company because they obviously did not know why they were laughing.

After a few seconds, which were enough to redden Rag's face, Mahinder Partap Sekhon stopped "He is Bhim Singh not Bhim Sen Joshi. Bhim Sen Joshi is an eminent classical singer. I think you are expected to know this much. Anyway sit down."

It seemed he was fed up of introductions. Good for others. He then stood up to take his favourite pose, awkward and amusing. As he stood next to the chair, one of his legs folded at knee rested on the chair, he himself inclined to rest his elbow on the folded leg.

Engrossed in that first sight, we spent the first period with him looking at the chair, crumbling, screeching at points. We all prayed inside for the chair for it looked as if it might meet its end anytime. The overall picture reminded us of a hunter, after a good kill posing with his prey for the day. As he mounted his thunderous leg on the chair day after day, we realized the tolerance of JNU's meek wooden chairs. They had withstood brutal force for years silently. Although an usual sight everyday, it amused us how different people found their comfort in different positions.

Another thing we were assured of in his class was that he personally did the *subzi* shopping because he had the complete, updated rate chart of vegetables which he brought up in one way or the other.

MPS was a perfect example of a tough exterior with a soft interior. After that whenever any of us spotted a broken chair in the Centre, we wondered whether it had met with its sorry fate under one particular Prof's weight.

Next in the faculty catalogue comes **Saxena Sir**, the ever smiling Prof. who was diagnosed with a perfect case of amnesia by the class. His charming entry with a grin without reason spoke volumes about his good nature. We sighed with relief.

As he seated himself, he straightaway started with his lecture for the day. His accent was a peculiar mix of French, British and American but his gaze was even stranger. He never made eye contact with any student. He just looked beyond all of us, straight upward. His gaze transfixed at a point in the horizon of ceiling and wall of the classroom. While he lectured with gay abandon oblivious of our presence and absence (he looked as if he could carry on the same lecture even if the class was empty) the class busied itself with everything other than listening to him.

First ten minutes we waited for his gaze to return to us, but it did not. Once assured about the lasting nature of gaze, the intelligent beings in class decided not to waste time. A few of them got busy completing assignments for the next class, another 3-4 went about scanning *The Hindu*, the rest, mainly UPSC aspirants made notes from the Spectrum guide.

In the meantime, his exotic accent and unique gaze had activated the laughter chord in me and I was laughing uncontrollably unstoppably with my hands urgently covering my mouth so as 'not to let a hiss. Also not wanting to be caught red-handed laughing, I enacted repeatedly as if my pencil was falling under the bench. Then I would slip under the table and let my laughter out. That day I learnt how sometimes suppressing a good laughter could result in a greater emergency than suppressing nature's call or thirst.

Days passed and Saxena's class remained as chaotic as Delhi's traffic. While he kept himself busy staring at the ceiling assuming that everything was hunky dory in his class, UPSC aspirants like Adhbhut and his types had completely disappeared from Saxena's sessions. Only when the semester was nearing its grand finale, did those faces reappear among us regulars.

One of those last days Saxena caught us unaware. His gaze suddenly lowered without warning and met our eyes. His first victim was me. He shrunk his eyes as if to look at me more carefully and trying to recognize or remember. Pointing towards me he asked "How come I have never seen your face before?"

Some matter inside me shrunk. He continued "Is this your first class or what?"

"No sir" That was all I could manage although my heart screamed 'Only if you had cared to bring that gaze down from heaven and bothered to look at the hell beneath, you would realize that I attended each one of your class.'

He lectured me on how one should not try to take advantage of a Prof's goodness. His glance moved on. Rag's face next to me looked like she had already got her share of scolding. But she had a marvellous escape because the glance moved on.

It was Adhbhut's turn. He had come to the class after months. I felt relieved that now this guy was going to get a bigger lecture and you know how great it feels to share a scolding. It is as if the insult that you felt just becomes half or one third or one fourth depending on the number of partners you have, to share the same scolding.

Saxena's gaze stopped at Adhbhut. His eyes shrunk again as if to doubly assure his feelings. But before he could open his mouth, Adhbhut played the trick. So, instead of Saxena's voice, we heard Adhbhut's. "Now don't tell *me* sir that *I* did not attend your classes. I have been regular throughout."

The whole class turned around to admire the confidence of the big liar.

Now sir sounded apologetic "*Arrey*, why are you charging me like that? Did I say a word to you? I am fully aware of who has been doing what and you have been quite a regular student." He stopped the exercise right there. The other UPSC aspirants looked at their savior, Adhbhut, with gratitude while I fumed, burnt and screamed inside.

After class, Rag wanted me to join her for a coffee at Barista. I refused and told her to go ahead. As I climbed down the stairs I met Deboshree, the smiling senior. As always, she looked concerned "Hey Kaya, you seem upset. All well?"

"Nothing, Saxena just scolded me for no reason." As I confided my little humiliation, my eyes moistened without warning. She sounded helpful "Hey you need a special *chai* to refresh yourself. Come. Come with me to the canteen."

She caught me by the arm and headed towards the canteen. As we seated ourselves, the first thing she did was order lunch for herself and *chai* for me. She then asked "You wanna have lunch? My treat."

I was in no mood to eat "No thanks. Just tea would do."

Then I told her my version of Saxena's unfair story. Fully enjoying every bite of her lunch she laughed.

"Hey don't worry. The entire Centre knows how forgetful he is. Nobody takes his scolding seriously. Do you know what he did once? He entered our class and started his lecture. Midway through he abruptly stopped, half of us were taking our afternoon nap when he stood up from his chair and said *Actually in the morning I had been to CP* *in my car*. We wondered what had that got to do with us. *After shopping I took an auto to JNU completely forgetting about my car. It must still be parked there. Can any of you*

---

* Connaught Place, central business area of Delhi.

just accompany me to CP right now? And this is not all. Another time he coolly came to the Centre in the morning and settled himself. As he saw Dubey sir outside the room he welcomed *Come, come Dubey Bhai, have a seat. Would you like tea or something? Actually I was looking for some important papers which I left right here on the table yesterday.* Dubey sir enlightened him. *Saxena Saab actually this is my room. Your room is two rooms ahead. The papers must be lying on your table.* He was visibly embarrassed. So never mind his forgetfulness. The whole world knows how absent minded he is."

She ended as she gulped down the water. Then she looked into her bag and an expression of shock spread over her face "Oh no! I left my wallet in the hostel room."

Left with no choice, I replied "Never mind, I will pay." And paid for her lunch.

She promised "But next time, remember it will be my treat and I shall hear no *bahanas*."

Reminding myself that this was the second time she promised this, I said "Yeah sure."

The next Prof. was **Kukumina Mukhopadhyay.**

The plump, cuddly, sugary sweet Prof. typically reminded most of my friends of their Mommy. She often picked up somebody in class and told her to wear a sweater lest she caught a cold. But apart from her motherly instinct I wish she had equally good teacherly skills too.

Every time she entered the class, she religiously took out sheafs of yellow sheets from her file and started aloud in a monotonous, unpunctuated rap, without the orchestra of course. She read out in one breath as much as she could and then to catch a breath, she paused, looked up, her eyes making direct contact with ours not through her specs but from over her specs. Once confirmed that the class had not yet left, fallen asleep or playing any mischief, she reassuringly went back to her yellow sheets (which seemed like the jewellery that passes many a generation in Indian families) and began another verse of rap.

Shubhra once wondered what Kukumina Mukhopadhyay would do if her yellow sheets flew away or better still were stolen by some miscreant. Would she then look up and interact with the students? Rag had a different concern. She wondered how this particular Prof would have proposed to her husband and whispered love messages into his ears "In this monotonous rap or what!" I on my part was reminded in every class of the *Puja* ceremonies we had at home where the *Pandit's mantra* sounded so much like Kukumina's rap. I sat there in her class feeling as if a Hindu *Puja* was taking place where the *Pandit* chants mantras in sequence, and one gets the feeling of something important happening without understanding and inferring much meaning out of them. In later confessions, our Bong friends who nodded nonstop in class also agreed with our opinion that nobody could make head or tail out of the lectures.

As for Kukumina, she could never figure out as to why students never ever cleared their doubts in the class and straightaway landed up at her home in the evenings. The queue of students was not so much to clear their concepts but to devour the snacks she served with her characteristic speciality, milk with Horlicks.

The final intro for this semester was the gentleman **Heerendra Nath Prasad** whom every body in the Centre fondly called "Heera". This gentleman was really gentle, never raised his voice, always came late to the class with innovative excuses like how his maid locked him up by mistake and how with great difficulties he managed, blah, blah.

Heera brought with him a Kinley water bottle because he did

not know what to do with his hands while teaching. He grabbed with both his hands the Kinley water bottle and rotated it while he lectured. From the speed and periodicity of rotation, we gauged his mood. If the rotation per second was very high, he was agitated and angry. If too low, he felt sleepy or lazy. This gentleman thought that we did not notice that the day he adorned his blue silk kurta he replaced his Kinley bottle with the blue coffee mug to class so that he looked cool with coordinated colours.

He had immense love for English literature and we never followed the content of his lecture. We just got lost in the maze of sonorous words he weaved to construct his beautiful sounding sentences.

Pinaki always carried his pocket dictionary to Heera's class as he believed in improving upon his English. Once as I went about praising Heera's knowledge, Pinaki interrupted "Let me tell you something honestly. Those who are actually knowledgeable, simplify difficult concepts. And those who do not understand the concepts themselves try to hide that deficiency by concealing the concepts with big and heavy words so that they can distract the attention of students."

This is what JNU did to people. They theorized about anything under the sun including Profs.

Coming back to Heera, he also mastered the bibliography better than the content of the book.

He wore tight clothes, probably to make his stocky figure look leaner. And finally this gentleman had a secret wish, which only he thought was secret. The whole class kind of guessed it right. The giveaway was his sudden move to sport a sprinkle of salt amidst the pepper of his hair, apart from a sudden beard again, his typical laughter and his style of speaking.

After all Amitabh Bachchan is not someone whose style can be left untalked about in India. Yes sir. We all knew about your secret wish to be A.B.

12

The Great Excursion-an abrupt end

Here the landscape assumes tremendous importance. It is important because it imposes, because you do things which you otherwise would not, you behave in a way you yourself could never fathom. As geographers it is very important to be in the extremes for a while so that you can experience for yourself how rationality disappears when survival calls. You live through a concept called "environmental determinism" implying men act the way nature wants them to.

Hills, better still mountains, exert that kind of overwhelming influence on you. They engulf you from all sides, your stature reduced to nothingness. Here, in confines of my cozy home in Delhi, I choose. There the hills choose and I carry out.

That June morning Mahinder Partap Sekhon briefed us casually in between his pan chewing.

"See, this is going to be a lifetime experience for you boys and girls. The hills transform your being. You cease to be you. Your friends cease to be the way they are. Everything takes a hue that is mystique. For example how many of you can now imagine that there is a thief within you, which will emerge when the occasion arises."

His comment met with giggles, cackles in chorus. He continued with utmost seriousness, mounting his leg on the chair "No, this is no laughing matter. Year after year our batches have produced such hungry stomachs in the hills which steal food. Your Toramal Sir has caught a few of them with his own hands. Toramal as all of you know belongs to hills. He knows them dearly, his Ph.D thesis is on the lesser Himalayas. Therefore the task of educating you people is entrusted to him. I wish you all the best for this journey which I bet you will not forget in this lifetime."

Toramal too was not ready to leave us without a lecture. Handing out pamphlets, he cautioned "I suggest you guys carry chocolates and dry fruits with you, they are instant energisers. And I am circulating this list. Try to stick to it. Carry minimum luggage. We've got to trek a lot there, so any extra baggage will be hard on you."

Rag tried to escape the trip by making some excuse but her only problem was that she got too innovative. To Sekhon she complained of kidney stone, to Toramal she cited gynaecological problem, and her fake medical certificate certified her unfit to go to higher altitude as she had high BP. Caught on wrong foot, she did not know that matters like this were decided by a committee consisting of both Sekhon and Toramal.

Hence her case was dismissed, as it did not have merit. Verdict passed.

However a few more who stuck to one disease were granted the permission to stay back.

So the CSODR bus rolled on with all of us fitted in.

We halted at Dehradun for a night and then via Mussorie we landed in Uttarkashi.

As altitude increased, the height of the trees decreased and shape of leaves became more and more needle like – a technique of self preservation that vegetation adopt. We made a note in our diaries.

By the time our bus reached Uttarkashi, it must have been around 11 o'clock in the night. The town was obviously not waiting to welcome us. It was pitch dark and drowned in dreams.

The only sense organs that seemed to function efficiently were the auditory ones. We could hear the playful baby Ganges twisting, turning and trickling around. If you pressed your ears too hard to guess the direction from which symphony of water came, you only ended up more confused.

To help our eyes use their sensory power we had to switch on a few emergency torches. In the darkness as Shubhra flashed the torch around to get a little awareness of where we stood, the only thing that struck us was a huge old gate and a grand billboard next to it, equally ancient, displaying paintings of ferocious tigers, elephants, lions and crocodiles. We started hazarding a guess whether we were to spend our next few days in a zoological garden with the friends we had just spotted on the billboard.

But Shubhra as usual offered the most logical answer "I do not think such a small town can afford to have a zoo with all these animals. So just relax."

Just then Toramal's accented tone caught our attention "Who all among you have a good sense of direction? The question is only for boys. This one is an abandoned park, a huge one. But like the rest of the region it has an undulating topography, OK? There is a plain spot somewhere in there, but in this darkness to find a way to that spot is going to be quite a daunting task. So the first group of boys will follow me to find the path to the plain patch. They must imprint in their mind the map of the area. That group will then lead the rest who will be divided into smaller groups. But remember, no exploring in the night. Everybody must follow the same path. The path that is explored by me." He added with pride. Some boys volunteered to lead the way.

After the boys left with Sir on the path finding mission, we engaged ourselves with the task of unloading stuff from the bus with the help of the remaining emergency lights. The path finding group was gone for a long-long time. We estimated the distance we had to travel after this long arduous journey in the bus. It seemed that our trekking experience was to start much before schedule.

A faint sight of light confirmed that a few of the path finders were indeed coming back. As the light drew closer, we could also hear voices. The leaders were back. One of them looked as if he had scaled a peak for the first time. With rucksacks on our back and camping stuff in our hands, we started our march to the camping site in small groups. Inside the gate, I could only feel the frenzied rustle of leaves, the trees around but if I were asked to recreate the entire path visually, I would most definitely fail. However after what must be a kilometer of climbing up the rocks, sliding down the slopes, we reached the camping site. The only thing I could conclude was this site had some loose soil in it so that our tents could be pitched in.

This little adventure had already consumed a good deal of time and it was not until 2 o'clock in the night that we got through with our first experience of pitching tents. Each tiny tent was to be shared by four members. It goes without saying that Shubhra, Rag, myself and Engli huddled together for a single tent clan membership. After exhausting the luminosity of all our petromax lantern, we managed to cook some basic *khichri*.

And believe me after hours of toiling in the bus and with the tents, even the hot steaming *khichri* and pickle tasted delicious with guys lining up for second and third helpings. They slurped-burped to finish it like street-urchins on a free feast and would have certainly queued up for more had the mess committee not shut shop on the face of growing demand and announced amidst cacophony that they had run out of stock with the khichri and if one was still hungry one had to do with the pickle only.

As one after the other, four of us entered the tent we realized how small it actually was. Once fitted into a certain position one could not move without disturbing the other. We slid our bodies into our oversized sleeping bags and zipped them up. There we decided to wake up at 5 a.m. so that we get the privilege of inaugurating the yet unsoiled broken room in the name of loo before it turns into a community toilet. However it was made clear the night before that the broken loo privilege was strictly reserved for girls and no guy should even dare to throw a glance at it—the entire nature was free for their use.

By the time we finally got to sleep, it was almost 3 a.m. Even in the literally tight circumstances inside tent, sleep is not a hard thing to come by if you feel like a labourer at the end of the day. We did not even realize when we slept off, but on waking up I struggled to find my watch telling me that it was already 10 minutes past 5. I tried stroking the three snoring tent partners but only Shubhra reciprocated. With Shubhra and torches, I ventured out in the unknown land for daily ablutions.

It was still dark outside. But Shubhra with her strong sense of direction easily managed to locate the tap, where yesterday we had washed our dishes after devouring the *khichri*. There we filled the bucket we had picked up from the cooking space and carried it all the way to the broken loo to encash the privilege. I never knew how it feels to do water management. Right there on hills, I closely experienced what people in desert must be going through.

Inside the loo I made a promise to myself "I will never ever marry a man from deserts, somebody who has done water management like this all his life. Eeks."

After the body bath inside the broken room, we headed to the tap under the open sky to clear the grease-grime-dirt off our hair. That's how we completed one nice bath – in installments – 3/4th in the broken loo and 1/4th in open. But the result was worth it. I felt fresh as a bird. On entering our tents with a lingering fragrance of shampoo and face wash,we found Rag and Engli still snoring. To plan our next action I checked the watch…..I rechecked it "Shubhra I think my watch has stopped working will you check the time in yours?" I whispered.

Shubhra checked hers and threw a puzzled look at me "How can it be 5:10 now? Wasn't it 5:10 when we just left the tent?"

"Yeah that's exactly what I am saying."

Shubhra constantly rolls one of her fingers around her hair when she is trying to rationalize something or she is solving a crossword puzzle or cracking a sum. Suddenly she extended her hand and asked "Just pass me your watch." One look at it and she smiled "Obviously, it doesn't have numbers or dots on the dial. Just the needles. So when you woke up at 4:10, you must have mistaken it to be 5:10."

"Does that mean that we have slept for just an hour?"

"Oh yeah! We deserve more. Let's get into our sleeping bags."

Once into the cozy sleeping bag clean and washed I knew comfort. As I dozed off, I heard slight commotion outside tents. Some people were trying to break records which were already broken by Shubhra and me. I slept like a baby and dreamt of my Ma cooking, my mattress, my family, my toilet. I knew their value then.

When I finally awoke, I found my snoring mates gone and Shubhra engaged in an innovation. She was tying a nylon rope across the tent to hang our undergarments so that they could dry away from the public glare.

"Shubra, you should patent this technique."

"Good morning."

"Where are the rest?"

"Out for their daily rituals. Shall we do one round exploring around?" Shubhra loved the hills and she didn't have to say it in as many words.

"I don't mind" I replied already changing from my pyjamas to jeans and putting on my sneakers. Shubhra picked up her camera, binocs and set out.

Oh God! The whole thing looked so beautiful, so pristine, veiled in a translucent dawn fog. It was an abandoned sprawling park, with rocks of all sizes around. We walked in daze drinking every bit the beauty of nature. Some of us were already busy preparing the morning tea. As we walked through the boulders, we spotted Engli and Rag in a queue before the broken loo with many more of our Maa Gos livening up the quiet atmosphere. We waved at them. Engli made a sorry face. Rag was too occupied bargaining, may be an out of turn entry into the loo.

Shubhra chuckled "Lucky us."

We walked straight towards the burble of the river and there it was, the youthful milky water gurgling-gushing with a mad determination in her flow. The park came to an abrupt end where we stood. Beneath us lay a steeply sloping long wall, like an edge of a bald terrace beyond which rocks and boulders of various sizes led to Ganges, not yet known by her name. She was called Bhagirathi here.

Shubhra pointed at a huge boulder of six feet behind and said "Let's climb that up. We can have a better view."

"Are you sure I'll be able to? I don't want to break my leg at 3000 mts above my home and limp for the rest of my life."

While I was still wording my caution, Shubhra was already half way up the rock pointing out the small protrusions where I could set my foot and go up. I resigned and tried. Half way through on the rock, Shubhra caught hold of my hand and helped me pull up and there we were on the balcony of world. Without any delay Shubhra got busy with her camera and I put the binocs on my eyes. After taking a rotation around we concentrated on the rocks in the direction of river.

Suddenly a head popped out amidst the rocks and frantically waved at us. Shubhra with her zoom and I with my binocs realized that the head belonged to none other than Adhbhut. He screamed at top of his voice "Go away you two. Let us crap in peace."

We laughed our hearts out and hurriedly rushed back. That day later at lunch, Adhbhut warned us not to stray into that zone as most of the guys were busy attending to nature's call there. Once they spotted us they stayed glued behind the rock so that we didn't catch them in undignified postures. I informed him in return that I would rather drink two pegs of poison than relish such an ugly sight. But that was later.

As we got down the rock and ran back to the camping site, my eyes for the first time fell on the boy, a local who had been hired for all sorts of help that a camping crowd might need. When he looked up towards me, his exotic *pahari* (hilly) look struck me hard. The charming twinkle in his eyes when his met mine, the innocence of a baby on his face mingled with the maturity of many wisened men, made his appeal irresistible and I knew at once that probably describing my own love story would be much more difficult than narrating anyone else's.

We washed our hands and made our way to the colourful shed where a beeline for the breakfast had already formed. Before my turn Shubhra told me about the discovery of how last night, instead of taking the straight way from gate to the camping site the pathfinders in the darkness had travelled more than one km extra taking one full round of camping site before reaching the spot finally "What a fool we made of ourselves!" While giggle infected the beeline I was lost in the face I had just seen, aware only of the closing distance between the face serving tea and me.

"Hey where are you lost?"

"No, no, just hungry."

Anxious of our first legitimate face to face, I was still undecided whether I should at all ask him something or let the silence speak. My turn came. Closing in on his face I noticed that he was much younger than what had seemed from a distance. His unblemished skin and rose hued lips confirmed that he must not have seen more than sixteen springs of his life. I suspect even fewer.

But the swiftness and dexterity of his reflex moves also suggested that in these few springs he has had experience of various types of works. While he deftly poured tea into my glass (all of us had to carry our own *thalis* and glasses) I observed him through the veil of vapour and promptly understood the meaning of electric current that runs in love.

I could not waste that moment, I could not resist it either. With a slight hesitation expressing itself in an extra dose of chirpiness, I asked in a rather pretending patronly manner, all to conceal my own feelings "What's your name?"

Not expecting it, he was taken aback but he lowered his gaze in a strangely shy manner and I instantly checked whether I had spoken the very words that I intended to or had I crossed the boundary of consciousness to let out a Freudian slip. I turned back to read Shubhra's expression that finally convinced me that I indeed had just asked his name and whatever else happened was between the two of us and the world was oblivious of it.

He replied "Abhimannu."

"Abhimanyu? Is it?"

"Yes."

"Or is it Abhimannu?"

"Yes."

"What is it, Abhimanyu or Abhimannu?"

I didn't think he could spot the difference. But the guys behind were creating a lot of ruckus as the breakfast queue was not moving forward. So I stepped back.

Our first day of learning in the hills. Toramal dressed in his red tracks divided us into small groups and took us out for our first exercise. Each of the group collected a hammer and followed him closely.

On a rather rocky site, a little away from habitation, Toramal taught us the exercise "Listen to me carefully. Take the hammer. Beat it a few times on the rock to be tested. Then learn to listen to what the rock says back to you. The rock will reveal its own identity. If the noise is *thak thak* then it is rock A type. If it is *dhum dhum* then it is rock B type. If it is *dhak dhak* then it is rock C type. If it is *tang tang* then it is rock D type and so on. To conclude I must say this little exercise is like asking the rock 'what's your name' by beating the hammer and the rock answers back. So listen with your heart and you will definitely know the answer."

He demarcated boundaries for each of the group. One had to

survey the whole area and report back as to which part of the area consisted of which rock.

After sir left my group, I along with Rag, Shubhra and another guy sat around the first selected rock. Rag took the hammer and beat against the rock "So what do you think? Is it like *thak thak* or *dhum dhum?*"

The guy volunteered "I think it was more like *dhak-dhak.*"

I couldn't make the head or tail of it "Why don't you do it once more, with a little extra force so that the sound is clearer and louder?" Rag took the hammer way up in the air and threw almost her entire weight along with the hammer on the test rock.

"Oh God what's this?" Everything around started shaking, the landscape, Rag, Shubhra the guy and myself and it was not until a few seconds later that earth was stable again.

Trying to regain our lost balance, Shubhra was the first one to understand "Earthquake."

Once the feeling of safety returned, I joked "Rag the *dhak-dhak* could have been less than this."

Rag laughed out aloud "Don't joke about mother earth, or you will do disco again like you did a few minutes back." On closer look we found that the tested rock had developed a crack giving it the look of a good boy's head with middle parting.

Whether it was the earthquake tremor or Rag's hammer, God knows! After faking the rock type survey, we returned to the campsite where the earthquake had emerged as the hot topic of the day.

In the pre-lunch hour, most students utilized their time to butter Toramal who would finally grade us for the great excursion, which was a credit course. We joined the crowd with an expectation to be spotted and noticed. Toramal was busy sharing *gyan* that we all pretended we did not know and took notes in the diary.

Phenomenon Earthquake – live experience on date 26th June '05. Uttarkashi lies in earthquake prone zone where tremors are quite frequent. It is located in an intraplate (between two plates) region, hence any movement underneath the surface manifests itself in an earthquake above it. A few years back, an earthquake devastated the small town of Uttarkashi which was literally resettled from the point scratch.

As I scribbled, my eyes drifted to the riverside where I felt aware of Abhimannu's presence. He remained unaware of my gaze on him and that made the moment so special. He again looked adept at what he was doing – fishing. I quietly picked the binocs from Shubhra's lap to steal a better view. First I pretended to look in every direction other than the river and then set my eyes on the target.

There he was. Teaching some of the boys the nuances of fishing with so much passion but so much of innocence. And I bet that bunch of guys around him who aspired neither for grades nor for buttering business were learning a great deal more than any of us, mastering the functional art of fishing. But my eyes were glued on Abhimannu and the ease with which he was catching fish after fish.

My attention was broken by a loud cheer around me "What happened Shubhra?" I whispered.

She replied back "Sir has just promised us a special lunch, arrangements for which are already on."

"Great, what's on the menu?"

"Freshly caught fish, the local guy has promised Sir." Rag added.

"Oh wow, that sounds awsome."

The protest culture of JNU does not die down even at 3000 meters from sea level. On hearing the menu, an all vegetarian club organized itself and within half an hour a letter was handed over to Toramal. Signed by all the vegetarians, it said since they were missing out the "special" of special lunch, they must be adequately compensated either with a paneer curry or a *mithai* which should be brought exclusively for them. To avoid further friction, Toramal accepted the demand.

With equal pleasure I watched Abhimanyu treating the fish with as much delicacy as a lean fish would deserve. After washing and cleaning, he cut the medium size fish at the right places and filled it with turmeric, salt, red chilly, pepper *masala* that he had prepared. He fried them till they turned golden yellow in colour. As I watched him from safe distance, I saw that even in his quick reflexes he displayed immense patience, a virtue so essential for good cooking.

The Maa Gos queued up like cats even as the frying process was still on. The fish was obviously rationed – one for each of us. As I looked at inviting fish on my plate, the aroma of cooked mustard oil enhanced my hunger manifold. I took one bite of fish in my mouth, it completed the experience as it awakened and massaged the five senses. The golden yellow beauty for the eyes, the aroma of spiced fish in mustard oil tingling the sense of smell, the spicy crisp delicacy tickling the taste buds, the tight texture of fried fish appealing to the touch and the crunchy chewy sound of the fried fish soothing the ear buds. As I reached the tail of the fish, I remembered the fingers that prepared this delicacy so delicately and for once the taste of fried fish tail arose in me a fantasy for the fingers who made it.

Pat came a smack from my conscience who poured a glass of guilt into my mind "Stop there. Spare him, he is just a kid" and

I made a firm decision to avoid him for the rest of journey. I confess that it was difficult, even more so when I knew that this relationship (if you could call it that) was a transient mirage, a quicksand I must steer clear of and certainly did not have any future. But again, I admit it did not rip me apart and I tried to label it as a crush like many of those that Rag keeps having like her daily fags. However the fact I did miss out was that I was not Rag.

I tried spending most of my days away from the camping site, away from Abhimannu in one of the small restaurants which was originally Rag's discovery. Its major forte was that it had a loo. So you could just order a tea, sit there for really long, relieve yourself on the potty taking turns and come back. By the third day, we did not meet the waiter's eyes. By the fourth day, he straight away arrived with three cups of tea before we placed any order. It was finally the fifth day when I broke my resolve and believe me I did not repent one penny for that.

As I readied myself for the day, Roly Poly ran to my tent "Kaya, sir is calling you. You are to be sent on an errand. Most probably for a vegetable and grocery one."

I walked to Toramal's tent with a sense of detachment.

"Kaya we just had a lottery. Your name sprouted up. So you have to do this entire list of shopping with the local so that we are well stocked up for rest of the journey. This is the last town on our way up where you find all this stuff. The vegetable from the *mandi* and the rest from the grocery shop. The local will be there with you. If you want more help you can take some one else. So you have a free day today." The guilt in his voice confirmed that the day was going to be far from free, but my heart was thumping for a different reason.

I deliberately chose not to pick any one else for help. First we decided to do the grocery from the nearby shop.

Much of the first few hours went by in silence. Once we were done with the grocery, we were still left with some time before leaving for the vegetable *mandi*. So we sat on a rock on the campsite and viewed the Ganges.

I knew one thing. If there is a love blooming between two unequals, it has to be the one with the upper hand who has to initiate the process. And here I was the upper side in matters of age, resources, education and all other things except perhaps height. It was a shaky start.

"Abhimannu, since when have you been here in Uttarkashi?"

"I have never been to any other place in my life."

"Have you studied in a school?"

"No but I have studied at home till my brother was here."

"Where did your brother go?"

"He died."

"Oh! So sorry. But how?"

"Jaundice, they say."

"That's sad. How many brothers and sisters do you have?"

"We were eleven initially, now we are seven."

"What do you mean by that?"

"As I told you, one brother died of jaundice, the eldest one – the only one my parents could afford to send to school. The earthquake gobbled down two of my sisters and one more brother."

I obviously ran out of words to console him. To change the topic I asked him "Are you the youngest?"

"Yes I am."

In a visibly shaken voice I asked, not yet sure of whether I really wanted to hear the answer "What must be your age?"

"I don't think I know accurately" I knew relief but he continued "but my mother by some crude calculation assumes that I am definitely not less than 16-17."

I knew further relief. I myself had not estimated him to be older than that. I settled for age 17 and quickly subtracted it from my age in my mind (21-17 = 4 years). Quickly I tried to justify my feelings by recounting examples of intellectuals, celebrities who had chosen to put love over age Shakespeare-Anne Hathaway, Audrey Hepburn-Robert Wolders, Goldie Hawn-Kurt Russell, Andre Agassi-BrookeShields, J.K Rowling-Neil Murray, Maddonna-Guy Ritchie. I had company, quite distinguished one at that.

I was still drowned in thoughts when a gush of gusty wind stormed in from nowhere turning the whole atmosphere hazy with dust. It was then that I noticed that Abhimannu was not sitting by my side anymore. When I looked for him I spotted him picking up my worthless classmates' undies from the ground which they so carelessly left for drying outside the tents and which now flew freely with the wind making for an interestingly embarrassing sight. I suspect some of the undies must have flown down to Ganges. And if somebody dared to ask me about their whereabouts, I could very well tell them to look for them in Allahabad, Patna or Sundarbans where Ganga would take them to eventually.

Halfheartedly I joined Abhimannu in picking up the undies with the help of a stirring stick that I brought from the kitchen since I did not intend to dirty my hands with filthy undergarments. I dumped them all in a single tent. "Bloody buffoons." I mumbled under breath.

It was already time for the vegetable shopping. My classmates were yet to return from their exercise in the evening when both of us entered the abandoned park in the CSODR bus with loads of veggies from the Mandi. The park again lay vacant with the exception of driver who was guarding the site. I suggested to Abhimannu that we could do some spectacular sightseeing meanwhile. We went out for a stroll.

"What does your father do Mannu?"

"He works in a dhaba in Dehradun. Initially he got us gifts from there, then he sent us money and now they say he has married someone else there. So he has not come for many months now. No news of him." His face grew sad and I thought there was not an inch of his existence which you can touch without feeling his grief chord and still these people lived life with such zest.

Again to change the topic I asked "So what are the names of your brother and sisters?"

"My brothers are called Rajesh, Dharmendra, Jitendra and sisters Sharmilla, Mumtaz and Rekha."

I laughed out loud "Are they really named after the Bollywood actors?"

"Yes. My father never missed any movie in the theatre even if that meant no food at home."

"Oh God! Then how is it that you are Abhimannu."

"An *angrez saab* has given my name." he said with pride "My mother was his domestic help when I was born. He came here to do some research on Bhima. My mother says he spent hours in the Pandava cave and Bhima rock in Gangotri. He named me after a glorious prince of Mahabharata."

How badly I wanted to tell him that the prince was called Abhimanyu and not Abhimannu as he called himself. But would he have known the difference? I shared with him some chocolates that I brought from Delhi. I could feel that he did his best to hide the excitement.

"Madam I also want to give you something."

"No, No, Mannu. It's all right."

But he frog-leaped straight to the only ice-candy man and bargained for a special ice-candy.

Before I knew anything I held a wine colored ice candy. I licked it and relished its exotic taste.

"Hey what flavour is this?"

"Madam this is Rhododendrons – the local flower. We make jams, squash, pies everything out of this. Do you like it?"

"I love it." And I suppressed my urge to go on. '....just the way I love you. Rhododendrons and Abhimannu. Hilly and exotic.'

Taking bites of my candy I asked "Mannu what is your dream? What do you want to become when you grow up?"

"Madam, I want to work in a big dhaba in Delhi, send money back home to my mother so that she can arrange for my sisters' wedding."

I was still mulling over the fact that how even their dreams have a colour of grief when another gush of wind again turned everything dusty and fuzzy. This time huge drops of rain accompanied the wind and in no time a wholesome rain poured. We ran for shelter. I could see a tarpaulin shed on a rock purposelessly standing, or may be it had a purpose.

Mannu deftly climbed up the rocks quicker than I could climb the staircase of my home while I struggled against the rocks which had turned slippery with fresh wetness. My feet just wouldn't find the right places. With little hesitation, Mannu offered his hand. With little hesitation, I took it. I think in this small relationship that we had, if there was a moment of consent from my side, it was this, when I accepted his hand. He took my hand and pulled me up.

Perched on a huge rock, both of us shared an awkward moment after our first deliberate formal touch. Down from a dhaba, an appropriate old Jagjeet Singh *gazal* played.

> *"Na umra ki seema ho*
> *Na janm ka ho bandhan*
> *Jab pyar kare koi*
> *Toh dekhe kewal man."*

(In love there should be no limit of age, no ties of birth, when you fall in love, heart is all that should matter)

'And how *Hindi cinema* has an apt song for the rarest of rare occasion' I smiled. I am not sure whether Mannu registered this moment in his awareness. If he did, he did not show.

He broke the silence this time "Madam, have you seen Govinda's new picture *Jodi No. 1*?"

I wanted to tell him that this movie was not new for me since it had run a few years back in Delhi. I wouldn't watch a movie like that even with a free ticket. But since it was the first time that he had revealed something personal on his own, I chose to lie.

Sounding curious I replied back "No, why?"

"It is running in the hall. I am saving money to watch it."

"Do you want to watch it tonight with me?" Did I at all realize what I had said!

He gaped at me and after a few seconds nodded his head.

"OK then meet me at the park gate around...when does the show start?"

"10.00."Dumbstruck he managed.

"At 9.30 then."

The rain had stopped. We climbed down the rocks. With excitement peaking in life, we raced through the marketplace to the park. My eyes captured a few small gemstone shops in a row. I checked the time. I knew I was getting late but on an impulse I entered a tiny shop to have a look.

Glitters and sparkles of rainbow colours enticed me from inside the glass. All the stones were laid on white fluffy cotton except one – a bright glittering deep blue studded in a ring.

I spontaneously asked pointing at the ring "How much?"

He retrieved it from the shelf "1000 Madam but we will fix the price for you."

"No no too much." In no mood to bargain I rushed out of the shop.

He kept crying out from behind "Madam, Rs. 500 for you. OK 300."

His voice faded and fizzed out …I did not hear the rest.

Back in the park nobody was worried except Rag and Shubhra. Actually no one had noticed as yet that I was not around. However, Mannu was much in demand and he got a bit of scolding for the disappearing act.

It was post dinner at 8.30 that I let my tent mates know of my plan to escape for the late night show with Mannu.

"Are you out of mind? Kaya, with that local cook?"

"No Kaya, do not get into unnecessary troubles." But I convinced them that he was a small kid with a small wish and the least I could do was to fulfill it.

Not that they were convinced but it is an unspoken rule among us that we let each other take our own decisions.

Around 8.30, I wore the only formal wear I was carrying. A burnt orange kurta with a brocade border, coordinated with vermillion khadi silk dupatta, sprayed CK 1 over me for my rather odd date.

Next I slipped to the gate with butterflies in the stomach and wallet in my hands. As I walked through, the darkness draping my entire being, a flutter near the gate acted as a signal of alert for me. To my relief the flutter was created by no one but Mannu. Since it was dark I don't think he particularly noticed my special dressing, or may be because it was dark I did not notice that he noticed, and we walked on without words.

As I spotted a small dim streetlight, I made it a point to walk under it. There I saw a look of compliment in his eyes, something much more than words.

A compliment to me would be brave words, may be a daring act for him, so I do not think he could come up to that.

We reached the small cinema hall, almost deserted. How I wished there were some more people around, this place almost looked fishy. The ticket counter said Front Row Rs. 5.00, Balcony – Rs.10.00, Box – Rs. 50.00. I compared the mismatch of prices with Delhi, put across a hundred rupee note on the counter. The ticket man cringed his eyes from behind the counter to press into me that I was overdressed for the occasion. He let us in early as we had a box ticket. But for the painted posters nobody could have guessed that this was a movie theatre. A small cubicle where I and Mannu sat side by side and watched Jodi No. 1.

The hero cracked jokes and Mannu rolled with laughter. My *paisa vasool* was to see Mannu like that. He looked so happy, seemed to be having his dream day today.

But just as we rarely see a dream to the end, some glitch spoiled the frolic of that night. Suddenly the empty hall started to fill up. It must be half way though the movie already. Who could be interested in a half-finished movie? Then I heard English noises in the crowd. In the dark hall, I could see black figures taking their time to settle, but something inside me unsettled and I was not sure whether this crowd was free from nuisance. As I focused more on them, I recognized some of the voices.

"Oh God! Mannu these guys look like my classmates."

"Yes Madam, I think so too."

Just then two of the guys turned around. I have no idea whether they saw me or were just surveying the architecture. But what followed was even scarier. Some other heads also started turning. I panicked.

"Mannu, is there another exit from this place? I think we must leave before my friends find out."

Mannu agreed "Yes Madam, let us leave. That exit is for the staff, but we can make use of it if we thrust a 10 rupee note to the man at the gate."

The butterflies that I carried in my stomach were on their full flight now. I slowly slipped and we did exactly as Mannu had planned. Once out in fresh air, it felt much better.

"Mannu, I must head for the tent now. If they have spotted me, the first thing they would do is check me in my tent." Instantly a cloud of gloom spread over his face.

When we walked back he tried to lighten the tense atmosphere "Madam what *ittar* are you wearing? I have a few *shishis* of *ittar* too which my relatives brought as gifts from Lucknow. They are quite well off. My uncle is a night watchman at a big office."

How much I wanted to tell him "Mannu, this *ittar* CK 1, even I cannot afford. Even I got it as a gift from my wealthy cousin who lives in NewYork."

But I don't think there was time enough to draw the parallel. A few feet before the gate to abandoned park under the dim neon light, I noticed he was no longer walking with me. I looked back to find him standing a few paces behind, right under the hazy spot light. The image of him standing in the halo of halogen, wreathed in transluscent mist seemed surreal.

"What happened Mannu? Do you want to say something to me?" I asked in hope.

"No Madam. I…..just wanted to give something to you." He unfolded a blue handkerchief and there it was. The blue stone studded ring sparkling even under this dim light.

Though this gesture of his touched me deep inside but I couldn't fight the suspicion that troubled me 'How has this guy managed this ring, he who was struggling for a movie ticket earlier today'.

I should not have but I asked curtly "Where did you manage the money for this?"

Wounded and hurt he lowered his head to answer in a hurt voice "I just took my salary in advance from Toramal Sa'ab. He was happy with my work so he agreed."

I felt terrible having doubted his integrity. But I think if there was a moment of consent from his side in this relationship, it was this.

Realizing the damage inflicted, I took his hands softly into mine and promised "I am sorry, really sorry. I owe you a gift."

His face regained its lusture "No. No need for that madam."

"That's for me to decide. Now you must go."

I hastened back into the tent without any accident. My friends, rather shocked to see me back so early gave me a quizzical look. I narrated to them the incident of the evening and sighed with relief to be back in the tent – safe and in one piece.

As they slid back into their sleeping bags, I quietly slid in the blue stone ring into my ring finger and pondered over the promise I had made to Mannu. Pop came the thought—'CK1. He had talked of perfumes rather passionately, but would he understand the value of it, the brand? Could I not give him something lesser? I should have some shame. This guy had spent most of his money on a gift for me when he is not sure of his next meal, and there I was – comparing values with his gift.' So I finalized on CK1, wrapped it up in some of the aluminum foil that my mom had insisted I must carry to preserve whatever food I bought. I switched off the torch and dozed off.

It was not until Shubhra violently shook me up that I woke up.

"What's it, Shubhra?" I peeped out of the tent, to find my friends standing in a crowd discussing something very seriously. I looked at my watch, 4 a.m. in the morning. What's wrong? I was alarmed whether the class has found out about my adventure of the evening. Shubhra confirmed "Nothing of that sort. Sir just wants everybody to witness this phenomenon of forest fire. Hurry up."

We were out with our diaries in no time. The orange flames could not be missed by even a nightblind. We noted in our diaries.

Phenomenon: forest fire. Can be caused either by natural causes like lightning or by human causes like a lit cigarette. Most cases attributed to human, frequent in Uttarkashi region. Results mostly in damages to cattles, wild animals and vegetation.

Unable to overcome my sleep, I capped my pen and slid back into my tent.

Early next morning I wore a fresh pink sweater and khakis which had deep pockets to conceal Mannu's gift. Now I could hand it over to him in an opportune moment. Outside there was chaos at the breakfast site. Mannu was late for work and Toramal was screaming "These guys, yesterday he took advance from me and today he has disappeared. Can you trust them?"

I felt like yelling "Chill Sir, your advance is right here resting on my finger."

As the day progressed, Toramal's anger mounted and so did my concern. It was in the second half of the day that my small world in the hills shattered.

Toramal came back upset from Mannu's place "Mannu got burnt yesterday in the forest fire. He had gone for his morning ablutions and never returned."

Shell-shocked as I was, I knew I could not break down.

So I escaped from the place, washed my tears in the Ganges, sat there and thought to myself 'Nothing comes as easy as death. It's finality decides that you don't have an option, so you don't have a dilemma. Everything else comes with a dilemma. To fall in love – Should I, should I not? To continue in love, to come out of love. Should I, should I not? But death is the verdict, there is no *should I die, should I not*. If I have to, I have to.'

Another gush of tears, another splash of the Ganges. I don't know whether the Ganges washes off sins but it certainly washes off pain....like a true mother.

Around dusk, Rag and Shubhra came to look for me. "Kaya, you are becoming so careless. Come on, pack your bags. Did you forget we have to leave for Gangotri? The bus is ready."

"Are we not trekking to Gangotri?"

"No. After Mannu's death, Sir doesn't want any more accidents. So he cancelled that trekking. We shall trek Gangotri onwards."

Another morning, another place. Believe me, it eased pain. Although it was yesterday but I was already in doubt whether Abhimannu really existed. Was he a dream? But then the blue stone shone so bright under the sun that I knew he had been for real.

Gangotri was an even smaller town, centered around a temple. This town is seasonal, functional only for six months of summer. In winter this remains frozen and uninhabited. People shut shop and return to Uttarkashi. It was outside the temple that I felt most painful when I spotted series of small gemstone shops with glittering stones. Some just squatted by the roadside with their stones spread on a dirty piece of cloth.

As I woke up early in the morning I stretched my hand out from the tent to retrieve the bottle of water I always kept right outside for the lack of space inside. Till now I had always managed to catch hold of the bottle without having to stick my head out in cold. But today the two litre Coke plastic bottle seemed to be playing hide and seek with me. When I gave up and popped my head out of the tent, the bottle had vanished.

I reached out for my pouch and went out to brush near the tubewell just at the foot of a sharp hillock. It was while brushing that I spotted Adhbut juggling my water-bottle, who was obviously returning from his nature's call from up the hill. As he saw me looking at him, he gave a remorseful look "We all come from good families. To crap outside is equally undignified for me and you, but you have a loo to yourself and I have to climb up a hill to relieve myself."

"Is that bottle mine?" Furious now I stopped brushing.

"Yes, you can have it now." He extended the bottle towards me.

"Yuck! Excuse me, I stored drinking water in it." I flinched.

"Drinking water or crapping water – all's same in the lap of mother Ganges."

For the first time I smiled since the tragedy.

"No, no my gift for you, you keep it. OK tell me, is it very difficult?"

"Difficult? Don't ask. Looks like the eighteen of us are not the only ones who use this hillock as their loo."

He continued "Day after day it is becoming tougher to find a place which has not since been used as a toilet. We call them human mines and by the way, how do you sit on a sharp slant and shit? God help us, if a foot slips, then in which pose I will die, only God knows."

By now I was roaring with laughter.

The journey resumed. A 14 km trek up to *Bhujvasa* via *Chirvasa*, both of them camping sites named after the trees they habited. Mules carried the tents and other stuff. We fastened the rucksacks on our backs and marched on – the narrow lanes equally shared by mules and human. The lanes permitted safe passage for either at a time and if mules came from behind, men always respectfully stepped aside to give them way. One error and you could land up in a valley where you will be declared lost for ever.

No bodies found, no declaration of death.

At a few small dhabas in *Chirvasa*, we halted for our late lunch. A plate of watery Maggie noodles costing Rs. 35 and a single *aloo paratha* Rs. 25.

While some of us ordered judiciously, some others were still smarter. They did small talk with most of us and under the guise of socializing grabbed one bite or two from every one with the result that they were the only ones with a full stomach.

The rest of the journey from *Chirvasa* to *Bhujvasa* drained life out from us. When I could finally see *Bhujvasa* I called out to Shubhra who was walking a few paces ahead of me "Shubhra, is that it?"

She turned back "Hey Kaya, watch out for the mule behind you." I turned around to find a mule clumsily chewing on to my rucksack. I carefully went sideways and let the mule pass. Later, I discovered the torn front pocket. The mule had a great treat of some Munch bars and Dairy Milk that I had stored in the front pockets.

It was quite dark by the time we reached *Bhujvasa*, and most of us felt crappy. After camping there, we looked around – the whole terrain was undulating. There was no place where one could crap. So in a group of 6-7, we walked in a selected direction. The darkness and the chill mixed to trouble us further. Finally after about two km, we hunted down a plain surface. All of us crapped there, went back and sent the second lot of girls to the same place.

We thanked our stars for the discovery and slept off. That was the first night I dreamt of Mannu. His innocent face reminded me "Give me my gift." I woke up perspiring, looked at the CK1, still wrapped still unused.

It was later in the day when we trekked our way up to Gomukh that our embarrassment knew no bounds. We spotted a beautiful tennis court decorated with mounds of crap at almost uniform distance. Quite close by, an army basecamp was at sight. Fully knowing about the perpetrators of crime, we gave equally puzzled look as Toramal laughed off the ignorance of the juggins who did this. Once Toramal went ahead, all of us had a hearty laugh.

Gomukh, the final destination, rounded up our experience. But the climax was yet to be reached. Finally food started disappearing from the kitchen. The pickles, milk powder, sugar, salt even uncooked rice vanished from the stock and the food stealing theory was reconfirmed with this batch.

However, it was in the adventure of night climbing that the trip finally peaked. A few, about twelve of us, hatched a secret plot to climb up the small hillock in night. A dozen is a big number, so the fear got diluted.

"Sir would never grant permission for this. So we have to do this without his knowledge but we must play it safe." Pinaki, the captain of the miscreant group, informed "First in the day time we must survey the hillock properly, second the torch that all of us carry for the adventure must have fully charged batteries. And one more important thing, since all hillocks are inter-connected, one must not mix up way to another."

That night Toramal went off to sleep without dinner as the kitchen had run out of stocks. For dinner we cooked local green leaves called *Rubab* which had a bad name for inducing farty tendency in many.

As night spread its large wings, the cabal' slipped out and gathered at the foothill. A stray thought again popped in my head. Mannu's innocent face "Give me my gift, madam." I paid as much attention to it as one should to a stray thought.

The trek began. We knew it would be difficult and that was the fun. What we did not know was that in actual life no such concept of night climbing ever existed and it was completely Pinaki's figment of imagination that we were executing. In no time the climbers got scattered according to their own pace.

Shubhra's torch gave away in the middle and I voiced my concern "Shubhra I do not think we should go ahead with it. I mean I don't think I was sane enough to agree."

Rag completely agreed "Yes, Shubhra let these fools scale up the Everest. I think the three of us should go back." Two out of three was majority, so it was granted. But majority need not always be correct. That was the wrong decision.

As we returned, we realized the hillocks just would not come to an end. We then tried another direction but even that would not end. Another direction and the hillocks ascended in height. Fear began to creep in, the enormity of Himalayan jaws sent judders through my being. My knuckles started to stiffen, breath swelled up, tiresome legs giving up.

Lost in the darkness, I would often ask Shubhra, catching breath in between "Are you there Shubhra?"

"Yeah, I am here. Do not worry. We'll find out." She reassured, her voice so comforting, her words encouraging.

It was then that the tragedy struck.

I stepped on, and to my shock, suddenly there was no rock beneath my feet, only air. I let out a scream. The adventure was complete. I was free falling. I found time to say "sorry" to Ma before my last breath. I fell and glass houses inside me shattered to millions of pieces. The shards pierced me. I died. The verdict. No dilemmas.

How do I describe my way to heaven? The closest approximation in worldly language – 'It is a watery feeling as if your soul is drenched in some fluid which cleanses your being before you enter heaven. An abstract floating existence where feelings are not as clear and concrete as on earth. When I finally entered heaven, it was a gauzy white-other white souls of men and women scurried about me, life in heaven is frenetic too but amongst all those faces, there was no trace of Mannu.'

It was not until five weeks that I was recalled to earth and to the realization that I was alive. I had landed into a poodle of water after my freefall, and became unconscious and the heaven was this posh hospital of Delhi where I regained partial conciousness intermittently and lived in a drugged stupor while I was treated for the multiple fractures.

Months after my recovery, on the insistence of my father I visited an astrologer. He rightly reconstructed my past accident. Then looking at a white patch on my ring finger he asked: "Did you ever wear any *ratna* ring before?" It was then that I realize that the blue stone had slipped out somewhere.

"No, no…. I just wore a blue stone."

"Oh no! I hope it wasn't a *neelam*."

"I really don't know but it must have slipped off in that water where I fell."

"May be it slipped off, and that is why you are sitting here alive in front of me."

A stray memory passed my mind once more.

Mannu's innocent face asking for his gift. Could it be that when he was talking of "His Gift", he meant the ring and not the CK1 perfume because he died before knowing that I planned to gift him the CK-1. An eerie feeling crept inside "Was Mannu acting as my guardian angel whom I dismissed as my inner voice?"

Next day when I reached the Centre, I straight away headed to the notice board. There it was. Another verdict.

All the twelve miscreants were to get one grade lesser than what they deserved. A special red dot against one name, that happened to be mine, meant I would get two grades lesser than what I deserved as maximum penalty.

I closed my eyes and smiled to myself "Losing a grade is any day better than losing a life. Thank God! Thanks Mannu!"

13

IAS Passion and Preparation

The preparation for Indian Civil Services is like carrying a baby in your womb for nine months. The exam itself is like the labour pain. The result in many cases a miscarriage. The next attempt is like trying to conceive again.

These August mornings and nights Rag and Rag's next door neighbour Ananya are both endlessly reading up novels, fiction, nonfiction. They only stop for their periodic food refills. The appetite for reading books is derived from the same cause and yet is different. Ananya has just cleared Civils, Rag just hasn't. After having cleared the exam, Ananya has nothing else to do. After not having cleared, Rag has nothing else to do.

This is the mother of all examinations. But for anyone who has attempted this exam, it ceases to be just an exam. It becomes your lifestyle, your beloved, your prestige, your tears, a part of you, your first grey hair, your hope and much more…..The exam transforms lives in one way or the other. It gives you what you didn't expect, it takes away what you do. It remains the mystery queen, wrapped all in veils, even when veils are out of fashion. This National hobby of JNU make poets out of the dry souls, mads out of counsellors, suicidal minds out of ultra braves and administrator out of….just about anyone. And it continues to spin different stories for different people.

Personal diary pages

Jignesh Chauhan: When I see my image in the mirror, I feel relieved. I do not reflect my family – conservative and rustic – whom I love but am not really proud of. But how does that matter? I am here for a cause..no….*the* cause, that cause which though unachieved, still fills in me the pride that my family doesn't.

But in JNU I see so many who are so much ahead of me, in front of whom I am scared to speak lest I speak something wrong, something stupid. So I maintain silence. I am quiet most of times and try to pretend that I know but won't speak. I burn my nights, studying. I spend my days, studying.

In class and outside, I keep quiet for lack of confidence and I am only happy to know that people around consider it my arrogance. I like people around me to construe my nervousness to be my snobbishness as that implies they see something in me that I could be arrogant about.

But sometimes I wonder if my cause is so distant, so far off, how can I remain so quiet, so lonely throughout the journey.

Then she comes.

At first, it is enough that she is a 'she'.

So what if she is not pretty, not beautiful, not from my caste, belongs to a State my parents have just heard of. She has spared me the time to look for a 'she' and the effort of first move.

Meanwhile I study and do nothing else.

Everything else she takes care of.

That is when all her shortcomings stop mattering to me. She

grows on to me. Her devotion, loyalty and love…starve me of my self-respect.

She only gives.

First she offers to do my assignments. I reluctantly agree. I am not reluctant. In my mind, I am just thankful, to God and to her. Then she offers to bring me food cooked by her with her own hands in her hostel room. I feel overwhelmed. Then she offers herself in my hostel room.

I am relieved. It seems like a worthwhile break from the cause. Such a revival in just a few moments. When all this becomes a routine, she indebts me. She takes my clothes to wash in her hostel.

As prelims are close by, she even carries the unwashed undies from the basket for which I have no time. This is that time when a tear wells up till my throat which I push back with difficulty for how can I cry. I am a man after all and I belong to the warrior caste over that. I would belie my ancestry if I start crying over matters as small as this. I can cry only the day when my cause deserts me.

However that does not diminish the gratitude I feel for her. The gratitude sometimes confuses me though, when I think from her perspective. She is doing her duty as any Indian wife should, wishing that her husband reaches great heights so that she can lead a better life and show off in front of her family, friends and relatives.

Then my own reasoning haunts me.

Is she my wife? Am I her husband?

In a few days time, the news *reaches my ears*.

The stupid girls of her hostel have protested against her because they believe, in a hostel, where girls don't have adequate water to take bath themselves, one cannot bring over her boyfriend's clothes and wash them.

They must have found my undies hanging in front of her room. Stupid girls. Why don't they then take bath in their boyfriend's hostels where they pollute themselves every night?

And what is wrong with her? How could she be so dumb, so careless? Why did she not dry the clothes inside her room, or hang it here?

I feel ashamed that so many girls would have seen something like my undies.

But I don't react. I pretend to have heard nothing because I don't have time from study to discuss such silly things. Besides there would always be the probability that she will stop doing it.

She mentions nothing of it in front of me. I don't know why.

Is it because she doesn't want to disturb or hurt me or is it because she finds it too embarrassing to mention that she was boycotted.

Nonetheless I don't have time for her feelings, not now. My exam passes. When I come out of exam, I feel ….. 'not good'. I should have waited for one more year, concepts would have consolidated in my mind by then. I feel wasted.

I start counting my scores, with dread and fear. I only count 20 questions per day. Wouldn't be able to digest more than that. It hovers around 75 from 120 in optional and 80 from 150 in General Studies. Only God had got me this far. Is it a sign that so what if I didn't know enough, I am just meant to clear this exam? However my friends believe I am a borderline case. I do not have any quota to support me after all. For the first time I feel let down by my warrior caste. I wish I could switch my caste only for this purpose.

Although exams are over, I still put my undies in the basket which she empties for me. No questions asked, no replies sought.

I sometimes weep like a baby in her lap, that is one more use of her. Life treats me miserably, the anxiety is too much. She calms me down. She mothers me, she sisters me, friends me....she loves me.

I grow increasingly irritant, stubborn but she bears me with patience. And then the result is out. I cross the hurdle. My happiness knows no bounds. I compensate for everything. I am a good husband again and she the evermore dutiful wife.

I get good grades for my assignment – better than what she gets. I congratulate her and ask how she manages to do a better job out of my assignment than hers. She just smiles back "Because I love you more than I love myself."

The dissertation that she is writing on my behalf is her final gift for me. After the mains, I will take over my life from her. To be frank, it is claustrophobic sometimes, to live like a parasite. I always want to be in control.

The mains spell disaster for me.

I cry like never before. I am lost. I have lost. I know it is a matter of time before she would desert me. This exam has drained out every drop of substance I ever had. Now I will lose her too. The thought sends shivers down my spine.

I haven't inherited anything other than the high caste from my parents but what does it fetch nowadays, nothing – neither in job market, nor marriage market. Moreover I feel I love her back now.

She doesn't do anything like what I expect her to but she senses my insecurities.

I bare myself in front of her "I cannot give this exam again. I don't have the strength to. By no means can I clear this exam."

She stands by me as a rock.

She plans ahead. Both of us apply for lecturers' posts in a small town near my hometown, for a meagre salary. When I disclose about her at my place my parents unleash their fury. "What can she give you? This bargain is a loss." I explain to them -marriage is not a deal.

We have our ring ceremony and the date of marriage is fixed for next April. We shift to the small town, but do not live happily ever after there. Being away from JNU helps, but the exam haunts me and I weep in her lap throughout nights. I even ask forgiveness for having let her down, but at least I know that she won't desert me like my cause did. I have tied her with the ring and got her away from all those boys who ever had the potential to woo her away.

We are at peace in this small town.

Then the miracle happens. I clear the mains. All my dying dreams come alive. I get that thought again. 'My sincerity has paid off.' God wills me to be that. I wake up and work with rejuvenated spirit. I just know if I have crossed that hurdle, I am destined to be.

The cause fills my dreams and days.

My interview seems decent, nothing to be elated about but not like losing hope. I can see a dream in her eyes. I am finally happy to have given her back something even if it is just a dream. I know it is turning into a reality everyday.

Finally the day arrives. I know I have made it, I must have. My name must be figuring in the list, then why am I so scared? Why do I not just go and check the result? I gather courage, all that is left within me, call up the junior Kaya who lives by UPSC* and request her. "Can you please check?" She has a sprain in her leg

---

* Union Public Service Commission, which conducts Civil Services exam.

but the cause is too big so she limps to UPSC and limps back. I ask with a shaken voice.

"Did you?"

She screams something so loud that I think the phone will burst but I understand and I scream back with joy thumping every corner of my body and existence.

"What are you saying, I actually got 33 rank?"

Next time, her voice was loud, but clearer.

"Not 33, 3…3 as in 3ʳᵈ rank"

Time stood still. "What is she talking about? Is she in her senses? Am I in my senses? I have never got 3ʳᵈ rank – not even in school!"

Then it sinks in slowly and gradually. Success seeps in. I have made my caste proud, my village proud, my state proud and I have made her proud. I give interviews, countless of them. I never knew there is so much of talk within me. I lecture on strategies that I know only now I had. I see the respect in others eyes and swell with pride. I see beautiful girls throwing coy glances at me with desire. I drown in them and flirt back, an art dormantly lying within me.

I am deeply soaked in success. Then it occurs to me.

I am too good for her. I tell Adhbhut "There is no place for sentiments within success."

He agrees.

I badly wish she hadn't done so much for me. Honestly, I now realize I was always good, only I didn't know myself enough. But now I know, the whole world knows. Even if she had not done that much, it could not have deprived me of my destiny. I was destined to be the topper. Besides who can picture her as the toppers wife?

Gradually cobwebs of doubts clear from my mind.

The main task before me is to break the news to her in a way that I am not held responsible.

"My parents want a *Honda City* for the marriage." Bewildered, she cries, howls but that makes me even more sick to be with her. And the resolve to separate becomes stronger.

A wild thought passes by. "Once she stood by me as a rock. Today I have stoned her." I laugh at the play of language, my ability to use language beautifully.

I will marry someone who deserves me or at least can pay for me. She belongs to none of the above category.

Today I stand to choose between a batchmate ACP[1], Tamil Nadu or a match of Rs 1 crore to marry. I have to choose the better option. I will. The substance that I am made up of, I cannot take a wrong decision. Can I?

Adhbhut Kumar: When I started from Begusarai, my place in Bihar, I packed in my bag two shirts, one trouser, some money, *sattu*[2], uncertainties and determination. I know I have to make it big, and making it big at my place meant clearing Civil Services. It doesn't get bigger than IAS there. I knew the journey is long-arduous-full of thorns.

I reach DU, my first destination and make use of that platform. I read a newspaper of which I understand very little but I don't give up. In mornings I attend my classes, in evenings my English speaking course. I read the NCERTs, re-read them. I move in with a person whose experience in UPSC I internalize. I read notes he gets from coaching classes.

I read magazines he subscribes to.

---

1. Assistant Commissioner of Police.
2. Staple food made of ground cereals, pulses.

He thinks I am too naïve, too young. So he considers me neither a partner nor a threat.

But I am determined, even more, to hit back, when people shoo me away. The anger in me propels me to study.

Then I reach JNU, my second destination. I see people clearing it before me, besides me, near me. That awakens within me the passion to give it my all. Those days I also enter the deep dark world of JNU, a clandestine arrangement.

I lie down next to a girl called Stella. In daytime we pass each other on road as if we didn't know each other. At nights she is the closest that I ever got to any person. Her touch is silky and she wears better brands than I do but I dare not ask her any thing.

That may jeopardize whatever little I have. Also I yet don't understand her accent so well. She is like a love making machine to me, inanimate. I must admit that more than any ecstasy, I was enticed by the human touch – the comfort of touch therapy.

Before she enters my room and body, I keep two hundred rupee notes safe beneath the bulky Spectrum Guide on my study table which she quietly tucks away in the back pocket of her Levis jeans while I pretend to sleep after the act, partly to save the embarrassment, guilt of the act, partly to make her job easy. But I can't afford her every night.

At nights, I yearn for a relationship, doesn't she? Sometimes I look at our jeans on the chair entangled and intertwined. I feel they share a better chemistry than we do. The He-Lee Cooper and She-Levis.

But she rejuvenates me for my mornings when I study uninterrupted for straight fourteen hours with time out for basics.

For days altogether, I feel there is no stopping me from reaching my goal. Those days I feel the world is beautiful, people's smile genuine, their talk encouraging and myself confident. I feel I can take on the world. Then for days, I feel nervous, shaky inside just at the thought of the distance from my goal.

I remember the face of all those brilliant ill-fated guys who never made it, for no reason. How their lives have turned into ashes and how they drink day and night. It unnerves me. Those days the world seems nasty, everything including life, love and conscience saleable. Those smiles fake and mocking as if to mean "Look at the village boy, trying to act smart. He will become IAS!" My head spins and I avoid people's gaze. I wish I could be all by myself. Rags and Kaya complain of my mood swings. What do they understand of hardship, they who got everything on platter?

I ache to be stable. I ache for someone to care for me and then I meet Peter. He is Stella's brother. She requests me to let him stay on in my room for a while. After what I do to her it is ironical that she finds me a 'safe guy' as she calls me.

Stella's 'not so little' brother stays on with me and when I lie down in darkness with him by my side, I almost chance upon the comfort that I search for in a relationship that Stella fails to provide. What elates me most is that finally I am not in one way traffic, he too reciprocates and I don't need Stella anymore.

This arrangement seems most suitable. It calms me for my studies. It is not extracting, not demanding, and not distracting either.

I give my first prelims. It is some experience. After all that I study for all those years the question paper still looks unfamiliar. I tell myself that I anyway did not ever expect to clear this exam in one go, but I must do my best. I tick answers which I think are correct. I come out and puke. The unease within me reduces. Putting your life at stake is quite an unsettling experience.

I can't let go of Peter but I don't feel complete with him. I crave for a woman in my life but do not have time to look for one. Sometimes I feel alien to my own psyche. Do I know at all who I am?

I have fixed up two juniors to finish up my pending assignments for Centre. They charge Rs. 30 per assignment and Rs.100 per term paper. But what do you expect out of undergrads in French? Only if someone could just go and sit for me in those end sems also.

My scores surprisingly add up to a decent one. I should be comfortably in to give the Mains. Now I don't admit anyone to my room. I study like mad. Even daily ablutions seem a waste of time. I study till I crash on bed. There is an obsession, an addiction in this exam.

The news comes. I clear the Prelims.

How I do in the Mains, frankly I don't know, I don't have any yardstick to measure. I don't think it's great as there is a lot of scope for creative writing. It is funny but I confess I draw grass and deer and lion and colour them too to show a food chain.

I am in abstinence. It is a resolve within me, just till the results. But my mind doesn't know peace. It wanders, feeds on negativity, and shakes me from within. Over and above that this is the second memo from the centre. If I don't show my face now, they will probably throw me out of JNU.

So I go in the mornings to CSODR, where the Profs find a new goat to thrash publicly. In the evenings I join *Vipasana* Meditation classes to ward off the negativity within me. It is not good for the interview. What if they sense it?

Time doesn't pass quickly but the day arrives. I have cleared. I am on my toes.

In mock interview sessions, they tire me out. I don't seem to be getting anything right.

There is a fault with my walk, the way I talk, what I talk, my body language, my expression. Huh! It is too much to ask for, to change my entire persona in 15 days time.

The interview is nothing like what I thought.

The only striking part is when they ask "Where would your hands be, when you are giving a speech?"

This is nothing like what I prepared. My thought process erred. I did not know what I would do if such a situation arises.

I rested my hands on my knees and replied "May be like this." I think now what an idiot I could be. Speeches are delivered standing up. Otherwise it was OK. No one has ever treated me with as much importance as the UPSC Board members did.

But I fail.

My world comes crashing down. The bungalow, the Ambassador, the red light on top, all of it blur with my tears. I don't go out for days. When I do, I feel everybody is staring at me with pity and sympathy. One more memo from the Centre is lying on my table. I let it. I hear so many knocks on my door. I don't open.

What's wrong with this place? More people come to console you than to congratulate you.

But there is relief in JNU, both relief and pain. Relief because you see so many of them, better than you, rotten and beaten by this exam. So you do not feel alone. Pain, because you know you can be one of them, beaten to the extent that you cannot rise again. I have no will, no energy left for this Prelims (for the next batch). But that fateful day my brother arrives early morning to wake me up and send me to the exam. You must be wondering how I have never mentioned my brother before. Because that is the role he plays in my life – nondescript.

I feel heaviness in my head and pukish. I could puke on the answer sheet, on the guy sitting right in front or in the scanty gap between two desks but I manage not to.

What I do in the exam, I could not have done worse.

My scores prove it.

I know with no amount of luck can I clear this exam.

My dream is over. I weep loud like a baby behind closed doors. I am scared of myself. I am beating my head against the wall, my knees against the table, wishing some physical pain inflict me so that I can suppress the depression.

One day I try to play football in the room. I hurt my foot, it sprains. That is when the miracle happens, I clear the Prelims. That is when I see another memo from the Centre with a final warning to show my face. Why do they love my face when I hate it myself!

I look at the sprain and decide. It is divine intervention. I confide in my brother, he spreads the word that I have not cleared. I plaster my leg and go into exile.

My mains are a smooth go compared to last time but with an exam like this who can say?

I clear my mains and in my interview board I enact the rehearsed persona, tailor-made to suit the idea of a perfect bureaucrat. This was specially designed by the coaching centre for me for the interview.

Finally the day arrives. D Day. When lives are made and ruined. Dreams turn into reality or crash against reality. The news spreads like fire.

Jignesh Chauhan has got the 3rd rank.

I can't believe my ears! That dumb senior of mine has got 3rd rank. What kind of exam is this? There is not an iota of doubt, I must have cleared this exam.

I take off my false plaster (my official reason for absence from the Centre) and rush to the phone booth. I call up Kaya, who lives near UPSC.

"Hey can you find my result? And yes check from top downwards."

She tells me that her leg is sprained but she will go for my sake.

Minutes pass by like years.

Finally the voice, her screaming voice despite the glitches of telephone line.

"What?" I scream back. "Is it 7th? "

This time her voice rings clearer "No 77th" she screams. I take a second, count in my mind. I will get IAS because of my OBC* quota.

"OK, great I shall visit you in sometime."

I rush to fetch Rags on a borrowed bike.

She by my side, I feel something inside me sing.

I know a new feeling I have never known.

Happiness oozes from every pore and you suddenly do not know how to manage all this. The thumping joy has to be contained. I tell Rags to wait for a second, rush to my room, bolt my door, beat my head against the wall, and push my knees against the table so that the happiness knows its bounds.

Then I emerge a little relaxed. The song within me becomes a hum. I zigzag my bike on road, break rules, and jump signals.

On one such signal a constable rushes to me raising his stick as

---

* Other Backward Classes.

if to beat me. Words slip my mouth without me realizing.

"Bloody he can not do this to me any more. I am an IAS."

I let the matter rest by pushing a 50 rupee note in his pocket. After the party that night when I lay down on my bed I was still not satiated. I wanted to stand up on the tallest building of JNU, the nine-storey Central Library, blow a trumpet like they did back home when a polio programme was due, and shout "Listen, listen, listen Mr. Adhbhut Kumar is now an IAS."

Early morning I did the closest approximation to my wish, I opened an Email-account.

"AdhbhutKumarIAS@rediffmail.com" and mailed everyone about the news from that id.

Kaya Pattnaik:

Ragini and Shubhra tease me the whole night about my Dad's adventure. My father has this thing for astrology. Yesterday I and Shubhra went to this astrologer who has predicted that I will clear civils in 2007. But he has told me to give IFS as my preference, not IAS. Huh! I want to be a lecturer.

Forward to 2006: After not clearing this exam once, it has taken its toll on me. I am a bundle of nerves.

I am not used to the endless hours of study. But I see Ragini studying and cannot afford to stay behind. Sometimes I doubt my own sincerity.

I can't get myself to go to that bloody coaching centre. Looking at the wretched condition there I never wanted to take admission but once Ragini insisted that it is the best available, I know no way else. I don't want to be left behind but I can't get myself to sit there. The stuffy room resembles a Delhi Transport Corporation bus where everyone's elbowing each other out. Different foul smells of sweat merge and float in the air. I have never felt more inefficient.

I can't concentrate on what the teachers are saying.

Then I see Ragini so completely devoted, not missing a single class, writing every word diligently. It scares the hell out of me to see the sincerity. I shift to the hostel to imbibe within me that sense of sincerity but that doesn't help. In the coaching centre, I look at her engrossed face and think to myself 'Is she not feeling claustrophobic among these many bodies stuffed in? What if a fire breaks out? All of us will turn into ash. With such a crowd you cannot afford to move your leg an inch leave alone exit the place. Is she not getting choked by the filthy smell of sweat? What makes her go on?'

But I thank God that I have her by my side. I take her notes, photocopy them. After a few days I decide I just can't get myself to sit there. Stacks of photocopied notes, with different handwritings pile up on my table. The process changes everyone churning in it.

I have stopped meeting friends, watching movies, even thoughts of Abhimannu have dried up. The only urge I take on from Ragini is the OCD of shopping. Studying on my table for long hours, I suddenly feel a dark gloom set over me, then arises the desperate need to shop. I look into my wallet, I don't have enough money to buy a notebook. Oh God! Why am I always broke? Then I seek the help of my memory. Whom do I already owe money? Who are the ones I have repaid?

Whom can I go to? My mind races.

After zeroing in on the person, I borrow money and buy a few kurtas from Fab, kurtas I have no place to wear to since I don't even go to coaching anymore. I try those clothes on and gloom fades.

But the tension of Civils is an all pervasive one. Only those who take the dip relate to each other.

I envy Ragini's devotion. I fear once she clears Prelims, there is no stopping her.

Well putting in our everything into it, the night before Prelims, Engli, Ragini and I go to my place. That we always do before an important exam.

There, we sleep rather we don't sleep, lie next to each other. The air heavy with the burden of tension, unease, frustration of three UPSC candidates before exam. I feel a chill within me; want the fan off, Ragini with the heat rising to her head wants the AC on.

Morning after that I see Ragini's swollen face, I know she is unwell but I am nauseous too. The exam breaks me from within. I can feel tears well up within me in the hall itself. Is this why I studied day and night? To play this guess game? By the time I come out of the hall, I can't hold myself straight. I know another year of gruelling hard work lies before me. I book a ticket to Orissa for a vacation. When I come back I count the scores. I scream with disbelief. It's a miracle. I have a phenomenal score.

I rush to tell Ragini, she is smiling back. She too has a great score. Both of us sit and compare. To our relief, we are finally clearing and doing it together – our "Operation SAI" (Reverse of IAS). We discover that in the groups around us we have the highest scores but something in us doesn't let us study. I do all that I missed out on. Watch movies, meet friends, buy clothes. I don't know about Ragini. She doesn't come with me. She claims she doesn't study but I have my doubt because as I bump into her room without notice, I catch her studying. That gives me strange sensations.

What if I am left out? What if she manages to? No that can't be.

I can neither study nor enjoy. I take to my old habit. I fag. That eases me a bit. I'm not doping at least. When the result *comes*, I become a nervous wreck. I have cleared, she hasn't. I wonder where she messed up – with her roll number or what but she is not that type of person. I thank God that I was spared the accident.

But my own condition isn't any better. I haven't read one word since Prelims. I always thought Ragini and I could face it together. With her gone now I don't know how to do it, all in two months. Would she mind if I have her notes? No she doesn't. Is she a good actress or is she really that emotionally stable? I study and howl, study and howl and study. I live in the most inhuman conditions. I study to sleep and sleep to study.

Sometimes when I wake up in my hostel room, I find the filthy black cat by my side, on my bed. When I care to shoo it, it walks royally without any haste as if I am the intruder. Once on following her walk I realize, that during my five hours nap, she has been shitting non-stop. She has shat on my chair, in the saucepan, on my cosmetics. Haven't they learnt to quietly sit and shit at a place? Something burns inside and I, Kaya Pattnaik, aspiring IAS or IFS or whatever (who cares), goes about cleaning cat shit, the most stinky and humiliating experience I have ever had in life.

God doesn't care about my tears and I think of Ragini who gives such profound statements. "Kaya you are born lucky" I wish she herself has some of this luck. I weep and clean. As I clean the room with water, I realize the stink penetrates my nose and through my throat reaches my stomach which responds by sending back what it had. I throw up yesterday night's food. Then I go about cleaning my own vomit. How's that for a lucky girl?

That pretty much summarizes my mains, though I study as much as I can, such are the questions that I make up most of the stuff. Having completely lost any hope, I confide in Ragini about how lucky she is to escape this experience, and how next time both of us should go so well prepared so that nothing can stop us.

Post mains I feel like a rat out of trap. I go berserk. Life looks like life once more. I know again the grass is green, rose is red and the date today is....hmm... 12th November. I realize now that I have ended up giving IFS as my 1st option, a service I never wanted to join. Don't ask me why. Because that astrologer told me to. Because I don't want IAS either...... I want to clear this exam and get a job. Don't believe me, do you?

Rather than preparing for the interview, I settle down preparing for my next Prelims an exam where I believe I am finally going to make it. Then the results *come*, I know they have come to ruin me. I have cleared the Mains. What, how, why? I understand the game fate is playing on me. I'll prepare for the interview but I won't clear that and without preparation next Prelims will slip out of hand too. This dream for me is over.

I join the same coaching institute that I had once escaped. They tell me that my presentation is OK but I lack content. How do you improve upon knowledge in three days? You don't. So God sends me to altar – the UPSC board interview.

On seeing the chairman of the board, the ground slips beneath my feet. It is the ex-principal of my college, whom I had once locked up inside a room with a group of miscreants. Could she have forgotten that? Her eyes tell otherwise. She has recognized me. My head begins to spin with fear. I am an intelligent girl but I falter and fumble... I walk out hoping they don't notice my grief. The worst phase in my life has arrived. I am introduced to a psychic side in me who can do nothing but shed tears. I thrust a pillow on my mouth, lest my cries wake up other hostlers and they complain about my insanity to the warden, who throws me out of the only place where I can drown my emotions.

But then I start believing in miracles. I have cleared with a rank 223. I have no clue how this has happened. Perhaps Ragini is right. I am born lucky and at least some things fall into place.

My visit to the astrologer of the eight boards, me chancing upon one that was headed by my principal; just about managing to clear Mains while getting record marks in the interview; within, I know I am more than lucky.

But I hear there is already some campaign in front of UPSC, some candidates alleging foul play in the results, and Delhi High Court asking UPSC to be transparent.

I know the questions boiling in your mind. Why are all stories winning stories, stories with happy endings, which is so far from truth?

In reality, only those stories finish here, which have met a successful ending. The rest remain half baked and unfinished and JNU is a burning oven of such half baked stories. The struggle of other stories and fates continue. Those stories are still in search of their ends. And how can such a story be yet told which hasn't found its 'The End'.

14

Back to Square One

"Throw the stale sandwich into the bin."

"Clear the vase of those wilted roses."

"What excitement? What is there to explore? We have been together for seven years now."

Like food, flowers and love, the freshness of JNU begins to fade as soon as your Masters are over. Suddenly one night you discover that you are no longer "a bonafide" student of JNU. Your presence inside the campus is not legitimate. To make your presence legitimate again you have to clear another entrance, the M.Phil-Ph.D integrated programme.

It was that night. Rag had crossed her 5 chocolate muffins, 4 cups of tea and 3 packets of Monaco Biscuits mark, her cut off points of tension. This night was months before Adhbhut and years before I cleared the Civils Exam.

Quietness in the room had made the air hang heavy over our head when I broke the ice.

"What a weird situation we are in? I mean if we clear the M.Phil entrance, it is no big deal...... as in there is nothing at all to be happy about because we are expected to clear this anyway, after all, we are students of JNU but if we don't clear, it's a matter of such shame..."

I threw a puff of Wills mild at her. She turned her face away.

Shubhra as usual was beating coffee for us. She tried to pacify us "It's OK. we will make it, we will just scrape through...no no....... what I mean is we will sail through."

"Come on Shubhra, you know there is so much to study. How on earth are we going to read through those many things in five days?" The heat wave had turned Rag's head cranky, but I understood exactly what she felt.

"Exactly. And look at me. What the hell am I doing here? I really don't want to continue here but just because I don't have the guts to try something new, I will write this bloody exam, and if I clear it I am screwed for life. I will be stuck for another five years minimum" I expressed my fears.

Rag's simmering heat burst into a volcano eruption now "Excuse me what do you have to bother about in your life? You have a home, good food, TV, nice parents and you still behave like a fool. You do not have to worry about a single thing in life, just need to decide whether you want this in your life or not, this much also you can not figure out for yourself?"She spluttered pacing the whole room in huge strides.

"Oh my God! Rag, you *toh* have to work in a *beedi* factory to buy your Fab India Kurtas every next day. Isn't it? And you have to clean toilets I suppose for your Barista coffee and Pizza Hut trips every second day. What deprivation in life?!" I butted the cigarette onto the floor soiling it.

The whole thing was taking an ugly turn.

Rag continued in her loud pitch. "My Fab kurtas, my Benetton

T-Shirts, my Barista and Pizza Hut is none of your business you don't pay for it so…."

I flung the papers I was fiddling with, at no one in particular. "I very well do. You have borrowed two thousand rupees from me and that is how you spend borrowed money. Rag, wake up."

At that point Shubhra, the pacifier intervened "*Arre*, what is this? Why are you both behaving like this? Let's stop this conversation right here. I am pouring coffee. Take a sip and chill."

I was just beginning to realize the potential of pre-exam tempers. I thought 'This pre-exam temper can ruin the best of relationships'. Just to come clear of the awkward silence. I said trying hard to sound chirpy and cheerful, "Hey Shubhra, why don't you pour me coffee in the pink mug?" "Shubhra, you very well know that I do not share the pink mug with anyone. That was my mom's gift to me." Rag retorted.

I had no special preference for the pink mug but Rag had pushed things too far. I blurted out "As far as I remember we bought the pink mug in Sarojini Nagar for Rs.20 from the *ceramic walla* who sits by the roadside"

I looked at Shubhra's face to remove the little doubt that I had about my memory. Her totally puzzled face confirmed my truth.

Rag was fuming like a roaring bull and I held a pink mug instead of a red cloth.

Rag got up from the stack of old newspapers that they used as a settee in the hostel "You know Kaya. I don't need to prove to you or anybody anything. That pink mug is mine and I want to drink my coffee in it."

"Very well then. Keep your pink mug and your big lies to yourself." I shouted back, walked out of the room, banged the door behind me.

I tramped in fast strides, and then slowed my step half-expecting, fully-hoping Shubhra to follow and fetch me and organize a patch up ceremony between the two of us. But nothing of that sort happened. I slowed my strides even further and dawdled around the same place but Shubhra did not emerge from the room. After waiting for a few minutes I stomped out of the hostel.

I placed myself on one of the rocks at *Sabarmati dhaba* that caters to Tapti too and recounted our fights. I concluded, by far this has been silliest of the lot. I could have ordered a bread omlette for myself but I realized I had not grabbed my wallet from the room.

Seated on a rock, I saw a *Neelgai* and in that tense moment I erupted into a smile. The folklore of JNU goes this way 'If you spot a *Neelgai* in the campus, you will definitely go on to do your Ph.D here' which at least meant for me that I would clear the MPhil entrance.

I threw a glance at my watch. It said 11.30 p.m. too late to head for home. It is such a nuisance to find an auto in the daytime, leave alone nights.

I got perturbed for a while over where to spend the night now that my ego prevented me from going back. I felt terrible for the evening and for the fact that Shubhra did not come to fetch me. Then on an impulse, I went to Engli's room. She was excited to find me knocking and contrary to my expectation didn't prod about my untimely entry at all.

I hardly slept. Early morning, I went back to room no. 101 to pick up my stuff, thanked God for the broken latch, pawed myself into the room and was relieved to find both of them asleep in loud snoring competition.

I had almost left the room when I thought it was indecent to sneak into their room without their notice. So I left a small note specially addressed to Shubhra.

Shubhra,
     I am leaving with my stuff.

            Kaya

As I rushed out, a small tear ran down my cheek making the moment so dramatic. I almost grieved as if I was walking out of a live-in relationship.

I reached home to find a whitewash planned for the day, which was scheduled to go on till my exams. A whitewash meant displacement. Displacement and concentration are not the best of friends. Worse still, the process of displacement had already begun. I hurriedly rushed to my room to rescue my books to safe havens (now that the prospect of studying together with Rag and Shubhra looked bleaker) but I realized it was late.

I stood in the empty space of my room, the blankness staring back at me, waiting to be redesigned. I asked in a resigned tone "Ma where did you shift my books to?"

Ma as hassled as ever was busy cleaning the other room "Well why do you ask? Whatever I took out from shelves, some of it is in the dining space, verandah or living room and rest of it I just deposited in Khurana Aunty's place."

I walked through the rooms like a zombie, glancing through heaps of important papers, office files, Readers Digest, Outlook, India Today magazines piled over each other.

"Lost in the books" rather "lost amidst information" I felt the lump in my throat for the second time in the day.

In the absence of any other sitting support, I sat on a pile of books and shed some tears to relieve myself 'I am not going to clear the entrance. How would anyone ever understand what a rough patch I went through not to have cleared the entrance. They will all laugh at me. Do I wish to clear this exam at all? I figured out 'yes I do wish to clear but what I don't want is to continue doing MPhil.'

Life is just so complicated even on such simple turns. The disarray in the room syncronized perfectly with disarray in my life. Just then my dad arrived with another huge pile of books tucked between his two arms.

"Do not disrespect books by sitting on them otherwise knowledge will fly out of your head."

"Oh God, the last thing I want now is confrontation" I lifted myself from the uncomfortable mound of knowledge.

I dragged my feet to the fridge to gobble down chocolate, juice or whatever goodies I could find to pep myself up. The fridge had also disappeared from its usual place but owing to its giant size I traced it conveniently, at least much more easily than the books. But when I opened it, even the fridge wore a desolate look, the stuff there few and unattractive. "Ma, now where is the stuff of the fridge lying?" I shouted still looking into the near empty fridge.

"I have given most of the things to Pati Aunty and the rest to Barik Aunty so that they do not get spoilt in these few days when fridge will remain switched off."

I went back to my book search. After retrieving whatever little I could lay my eyes on, I squatted on the mat to prepare for the exam lurking in front of me. How ever much I tried to study, the futility and uselessness of the effort clouded over me overwhelmingly.

The only thing that kept troubling me was the fight the night before. It was then that it struck me that Shubhra has not even called me up. I looked at the phone with a hope that it would ring now but it would not comply.

I did not expect anything out of Rag but I never knew that Shubhra could take sides, that too the wrong side in this case.

In helplessness and hopelessness I looked the other side where the old newspaper of Sunday lay scattered waiting with open arms to embrace the scraped off walls. I pulled the colourful supplement towards myself and looked for the Astrozone, my weekly horoscope.

Just below the comic cartoon strips of Dennis, Garfield and Beau Peep my fate stared back at me.

"*A few surprises and shocks in store for you. Be careful and restrain yourself. Ganesha warns not to get into arguments with friends and relatives. Not a good time for new ventures. New romance will bloom but some old ties will weaken. People in business, glamour world, and journalism will get good news but those in higher studies, research and computers should be cautious.*"

'Oh no only if I could read this on Sunday itself I could prevent the Monday and Tuesday from happening' I looked at the phone again with hope, it did not ring.

The next few days passed in adjusting and readjusting rooms at my home. Lifting chairs, dragging shelves, shifting sofas, arranging knick-knacks back into place is a great destresser and looking with anticipation at the phone in middle of things, the biggest stresser. Then it happened. Things had almost been restored to their places, though the inertia of disorganization still lingered in the air, Ma pleaded "Beta, I almost forgot all this while why don't you rush to

Khurana Aunty's place and register a complaint for our phone?"

My eyes widened till eternity "Whaa..t? The phone is not working! What are you saying Ma?"

I stumbled to pick up the receiver and found no dial tone. Ma's incessant background commentary didn't take a break.

"How much do you care? The phone is dead since four days. I was busy with the whitewashing but none of you even cared to check….."

With the dead receiver in my hand, I knew relief. I construed a story to my convenience. Shubhra would have walked till the *Teflas* PCO, dialled my number several times only to find 'no reply'.

Once I resolved my ego problem for the day, I went back to studies. Now that all that I had to cram lay in front of me, I realized there was no time left to go through everything. It felt better again to float back to introspect whether I should do my MPhil at all, if in case I clear the entrance. 'Only God knows whether I would get a chance to exercise such a choice, now that my chances of clearing the entrance looks lower than ever before.' When destiny blurs and you feel wronged, and fail to think straight, go back to sleep after waking up. A choice safer than smoking and doping.

On the night before the exam, my nerves crisscrossing my head throbbed persistently, my throat parched, even the weatherman reported the most humid day in the last four years and bile congested the foodpipe. I suspect whether an Iraqi soldier felt the same way when he battled it out against the US Army a soldier who seems more convinced of his own defeat a powerful enemy camp.

So after a sleepless, restless night and 2-3 bouts of vomit

threatening but refusing to relieve me, I set out to fight the losing battle. I bowed before God in a final act of buttering prayer 'This time Lord, only this time, one last time, I know I have said this before, but I mean it this one time. Please ..Please' and climbed down the stairs of my home. My *Ma* never shirking her responsibility, standing at the gate with that bowl of curd to inject some good fortune into my dwindling jerking fate sent jitters of shame inside me. "Ma what is the need for all this paraphernalia?" I said peevishly. She still wished me luck from behind, I hid my tears by pulling the eye curtains down.

On reaching the examination centre, along with a shoal of chattering candidates I trudged up the tattered school stair, and felt as if I was walking up to throw my prestige, ego to the large green dustbin which stood with its lips parted and an inviting suggestive message 'USE ME'. I looked away, geared myself with deep breaths. A small positivity popped up inside me suddenly, only to be washed away by gloom in the next few seconds.

When the question paper was handed over to me, I rubbed my eyes a few times to check whether I had seen the geography paper at all. I didn't understand why JNU Profs take it as such a challenge to set up a question paper as innovative as this. Well that might work for me since I realized the question paper would seem equally alien to someone who had burnt their nights away for this entrance as for me who had gone through the little big emotional upheaval and not studied at all.

Just when the bulbs of my knowledge were dimming down, my brain suddenly woke up to a ray of light. A flurry of activities, statements, images and ideas suddenly flooded my mind and aroused it. An idea clicked bright like a camera flash. If only I could pepper my answers with "Critical Faculty" as JNU Profs call it, I should be able to touch the chord with the examiner.

And what better way to demonstrate the CF factor than to use the very words of Profs in the answer. I used those very examples which were commonly discussed in the class many times over and year after year. These were the most talked about examples, typical, distinct and exclusive of the classes held in our Centre. Sometimes I found a context to put those examples, sometimes I imposed a context. All this while I thought of two things in my mind.

a)   If the examiner finds his own ideas staring back at him from the test paper, he has little choice but to accept them.

b)   Through these very examples I could pass the message across that I was their own product without any foul play since the coding procedure is an extremely strict one in JNU where in no circumstance one could find out whose test booklet one is checking.

Writing one's name or any other design would have meant getting disqualified straight away. So here I was without u s i n g any illegitimate means doing my job. Whether they would disown their own product was entirely their own decision.

My job was done.

I came out of the exam hall relieved but not content. I knew I had played a trick. Whether it would work or not only time would tell.

Back home Ma informed that phone had returned back to good health and first call had indeed been of Shubhra's.

The fight had completely slipped off my mind. Now it replayed and rekindled the anxiety. I picked up the receiver to return the call but put it down. I picked it up again and dialed the hostel number. Half way through dialing I put it down.

Inside I was craving to talk to Rag and Shubhra but I also felt the anger for having been left alone 'what if Rag came down to answer the phone. Then I would formally ask her to call Shubhra'. OK so I dialled the number.

The familiar voice of the attendant from that side rose above the banter in backdrop.

"Bhaiya 101, Shubhra"

"*Ji* Madam, will you hold or will you call after five minutes?"

"I shall hold"

The banter behind graduated to an impassioned debate on casteist politics.

After a few minutes Shubhra's voice echoed from the other side "Hey Kaya, I tried your number so many times. Was your phone dead or something?"

I was relieved to find that the story had unfolded according to my hypothesis.

"Yeah yeah it was."

"OK how was your exam?"

"Bad and yours?"

"I think worse. Everybody is cribbing over the question paper." I was relieved once more.

"And I thought I didn't understand the questions because I didn't study."

"No everybody is shocked about that one. Why don't you just come over we'll plan for a movie at Priya and dinner after that."

"OK I'll be there in an hour." I didn't dare mention what Rag'll think for the fear that they might leave me alone and have fun.

I reached Tapti with my overnight bag by my side.

When I entered 101, Rag and Shubhra looked up at me together. Time stood still for the moment. None of us uttered anything- the very next moment we all burst out laughing for no apparent reason. May be that's friendship, you can laugh together even without any reason to laugh about. I think nothing mattered more in that very moment than the fact that we were together again. Our laughter was put on brakes only when Engli entered with her hair all meshed up, entangled around a roller brush. Oh! did I mention that our Engli has become extremely fashion conscious and would not make public appearances without setting her hair with her new hair drier?

It was while disentangling her hair from the brush that I got to know from Shubhra what had happened the other day…….. *when I banged the door of 101 and walked in slow strides waiting for Shubhra to come after me, she had indeed got up from her seat to follow me but then Rag had burst into tears. So she couldn't leave her all by herself. By the time Rag quietened, I must have reached the dhaba. Shubhra not finding me in the corridors, went to Engli, expecting to find me there but by then I had not reached her room. After that Shubhra left for the phone booth to call my home but found that my phone wasn't working. While Shubhra was still away, I must have walked into Engli's room who in her stuporous excitement forgot to mention that Shubhra had come looking for me. Huf!* Life is indeed complicated.

After a boring *sci-fi* movie at Priya cinema and a delicious *tandoori* dinner at *Mezbaan* when we came back to the room, Shubhra in her ritualistic way sat down to beat the coffee. It was while setting up the mugs that I spotted the pink coffee mug in broken pieces lying in a corner of the room. I gave a hard stare at the broken mug then looked back at both of them. "Not me" Rag and Shubhra replied in chorus.

"Who then?" I asked back. Shubhra the savior came to ego rescue "Must be the cats who sneak in when we are out" To distract us from the topic she continued "Do you see how they lick the plates in the hostel mess? That is so unhygienic…"and we chit-chatted the night away as the discussion hopped from mug to cat to hostel mess to the uncivil guys in mess to which of those guys dated whom to their girlfriend's unsavoury dressing sense to the new summer stock of *kurtas* at Fab India to……..

However I still suspect that since Shubhra is not the breaking types, Rag must have smashed the mug, in most likelihood deliberately and was too embarrassed to admit it later.

A few days later, our class congregated before the result board. I and Rag maintained a decent distance from the board with our eyes shut tight as if that could prevent us from the oncoming storm. Shubhra, the bold one is always entrusted with the task of checking results.

"Rag" Shubhra called out.

The relief in her tone already informed me that nothing untoward had happened, at least not with any of us. There had been a few mishaps though, some of the names from the class didn't figure in the list but ours were spared. A formality of celebration in the evening was carried out and preparation for the next step began.

Since the reason for celebration wasn't exactly perceived to be that great, the place of celebration happened to be a small inexpensive Tibetan joint at the Kamal Shopping Complex called *Keicha*.

We discussed over our favorites – lamb chilli dry and garlic noodles with coffee for Rag, Coke for me and *nimbupani* for Shubhra. I wondered "How do you think these people manage to get most JNUites clear the written exam, irrespective of how disastrously one had fared in it, obviously they do not have a way of knowing, as the roll number is coded once more in Admin block and the system seems to be quite fair."

"That's true, it is quite fair"

Shubhra always has the task of rationalizing the toughest of question. "Maybe there is a sense of JNUness in the answer. Whether we agree or not this place grows on to you and grows into you. May be the Profs sense that JNUness in your answer and so they identify us."

I know you might be finding the conversation a little vague but that's true. JNU definitely soaks in your lifestyle, your worldview, your attitude and into you so much so that after a 15 minutes chat session, there is no way that one JNUite cannot recognize another anywhere in the world even if their conversation had no mention of their backgrounds.

Well the written exam behind, one had to finally clear the small hurdle of interview to be officially admitted to the MPhil program.

JNU is like a large Indian joint family household, full of customs and rituals. One of those is after clearing the written exam of M.Phil entrance, if you are an in-house (read JNU) student already, you must pay a visit to the temporary deities in their temples (read Profs in their cabins) with a face so humble that it should speak for itself. It should reflect "Take me in your *sharan* (shelter) God, I have come here with lot of hope. Grant me my wish and become my guide. Save me in the interview board, my lord and I will be your slave for rest of my days in JNU."

If the deity obliges he or she will accept you as a *bhakt* (devotee) and bless you with the *prasad* (a topic) of his specialization which of course is changeable and flexible once you clear the final hurdle of interview. But before all that you must pass through this small humiliating experience. So the three of us sat through the catalogue of faculty and discussed pros and cons on points like:

- ✓   Who is a hard task master?
- ✓   Who has better connections in places that matter?
- ✓   Who has good conduct?
- ✓   Who can spare you most amount of time etc. etc.

After considering our options thoroughly depending on which Profs we would like to work with, we zeroed down upon our areas of interest 1) literacy 2) health 3) crime.

The day you finally visit the Prof is a sacred one as I have mentioned before. Although one would not admit, but one does dress up in one's best attire in the wardrobe to look more suitable, praying to be picked up by the Prof. one had chosen.

That morning I put on a new salwar kurta recently bought from *Anokhi* in Khan Market. But one look at the mirror and I felt overdressed as if I was desperate to impress. So I reconciled to my old white T-Shirt and denim skirt.

On my way to JNU I realized that it had actually been two months since I last visited the Centre. Shubhra and Rag had put on their best attires, so there was an air of formality when we walked till the Centre. Since none of us were the real buttering types and had rarely visited Profs even when we needed to, the experience did not seem as easy as it may sound to you. At that moment we realized the importance of having wasted two years and not building a rapport with any of the Profs.

At the Centre building, we trudged up the stairs, each step weighing as heavy as thousand pounds but then a strange feeling began to engulf me from all sides. Suddenly I felt an inscrutable sense of comfort, an ineffable excitement in the Centre like never before. As classmates jostled around me, Profs passed me in haste and hurry, I could sense this strange familiarity and mysterious connection with them. That's not all, I could also establish an inexplicable relation with the inanimate things around, the walls, the ancient grubby half torn maps, the notice board. As I was lost in this new found awareness, the three of us had parted to visit Profs of our own choice, deciding to meet each other in the canteen after our work was over.

This impromptu sense of comfort helped me sail through my visit to the Prof. in a much smoother manner than I ever expected.

After my rather easy meeting where the Prof. had almost readily agreed to spare me a topic, I went to the canteen to realize that may be for a change I was the first one to be granted the wish.

Rag and Shubhra might be still engaged in cracking a deal in the floors above me. I walked in daze to the much in demand seat under the fan and ordered for a *masala* tea and bread roll. I still could not get over the overwhelming feel. But after a sip of tea refreshed my vision, I vaguely and gradually made sense of what I felt. I felt as a mother would feel near her child, a painter would feel towards his painting, a director must feel about his film and most importantly.........as an author must feel about his book.

As surreal as it may sound but I actually felt that these corridors, these walls, these political posters on them are my creations, even the Profs as they passed me are characters created by me. It was as if I was living inside my book talking to characters created by me. This I realized is the interface of reality and imagination. This realization brought a surge of an intense emotion within me and this indescribable emotion condensed into a lump in my throat and a tear in my eye.

As I reached the final pages of my book writing, standing in the midst of my book I relived those moments which have passed, the lessons which I learnt, the people who have transformed and the life which is spent here. My trance trip was broken by fingers which waved in front of me.

Rag and Shubhra were back.

I raised my eyebrows in a questioning manner. Rag replied "OK."

Shubhra followed "All right."

Rag asked "Where were you lost?"

I opened my mouth to describe the beautiful sweet-sour experience but then realized that may be I would not be able to translate the feelings into words or may be Rag would discard the entire thing as one of my *chaat* philosophizing.

So instead I said "Nothing."

But friends are friends. They sense it if you are trying to hide.

"OK if you don't want to share" said Rag.

"No really nothing."

Shubhra as usual came to rescue when an awkward moment is fast spiraling into an embarrassing one "Have you seen the weather outside? It's cloudy and breezy. Let's take our cups to the terrace and sit."

'Shubhra, the nature lover.'

We picked up our cups and walked up to the terrace, surprisingly empty at this hour. We sat on the terrace floor which was also the the roof of the canteen. Rag fiddled with Shubhra's bag, drawing out her permanent marker set.

She said "Can I take a little liberty with your T-Shirt? Its whiteness and this lovely weather compels me to paint."

"Would you listen if I say no?"

"Not really."

"So then, why ask? Here's your canvas" and I turned my back to her.

As she busied herself with her masterpiece spoiling my white T-Shirt, I faced Shubhra "You know Shubhra after my talks with Prof. Bahuguna finalized, I got up. As I was about to leave the room, I turned back to ask 'Sir do you think I will clear the interview?' Do you know what he replied?"

"What?"

"Beta it is very difficult to get into JNU but it is even more difficult to get out of it."

"How true!"

Rag from my behind "OK right now, right here each of us will in few words describe how one feels about JNU at this very moment after your Masters is over and MPhil is about to start." She continued "Shubhra your turn and your time starts now."

"I had no doubt had a blast in my masters but as I enter my M. Phil-PhD I feel a little jittery, kind of little worried about my future and job. This place has been great till now but today at this moment I feel the hands of the clock will stop and start moving anticlockwise for those of us who stay here. Also I feel this must be the only campus where partings rather than meeting of friends is celebrated, I mean in a metaphorical sense, isn't it? When friends get together they crib about not having a job and only when they leave the campus for a job, it is a real celebration time."

Claps. "Nice little few words or speech shall I say. Kaya your turn now."

"I feel JNU is like an old T-Shirt, which you know might not look great on you anymore, but you are so comfortable in it that you are not ready to part with it."

Claps again. "Not bad, not bad at all."

"And what about you Rag! Your turn."

"OK you turn your back to Shubhra."

I obeyed and Shubhra read it aloud.

"She has drawn a cobweb with the black marker.

Below that there is message in red.

"You cannot win

You cannot break even

You can't even quit the game."

"That's creative but that was not the game you cheater. OK. Let me lay the rules for this one" I said "We have to write and describe in three to four words exactly the way you feel now about clearing the M.Phil Entrance." I took out my notepad and tore three pages from it. After secretly jotting our messages on the chits we folded the papers and tossed it on to floor.

Rag pulled out one folded paper and opened.

It was Shubhra's. She had written

"Back to the start."

I opened another it was Rag's, it said

"Back 2 ◻ 1"

Shubhra unfolded the last one, my chit

"Back to square one"

We laughed with disbelief as we realized that how JNU had sharpened our "critical faculties" to standardize even our thought process.

We laughed again as a gush of sweet breeze caressed our cheeks and engulfed our existence. I felt as if JNU just squeezed our cheeks, ruffled our hair and gave us a warm hug. If only I could seize that moment and hold the time.

Feed back

Engli: Why are the anonymous conversations so dry? You must jazz them up with the quintessential abuses. No one ever talks here without paying a nasty tribute to the other's mother and sister. You must pepper the talks with *Galis* to make it sound more realistic.

Rag : Why have you made my boyfriends leave me all the time. I don't like that aspect of your book. Instead make me dump them.

Shubhra : When will you complete the book? Will you ever complete it?